BRAIN GAMES BRAIN POWER

MORE THAN 250

✳ WORD GAMES ✳ LOGIC PUZZLES
✳ NUMBER CHALLENGES ✳ TRIVIA QUIZZES

Trusted
Media
Brands

New York / Montreal

D1403964

Copyright © 2020 Trusted Media Brands, Inc.
All rights reserved. Unauthorized reproduction, in any manner, is prohibited.

ISBN: 978-1-62145-515-8

Printed in China

10 9 8 7 6 5 4 3 2 1

Note to Readers

The consultants, writers, editors, and proofreaders have taken all reasonable measures
to confirm and verify the accuracy of the information contained in this title. However,
some statements of fact can be open to interpretation. Similarly, new information and
research often reveal that long-held beliefs are not true. We welcome your input on
any answers for which you have sound evidence may be incorrect.

STAY SHARP, STAY YOUNG

The puzzles in this book may help you improve a variety of brain skills, including your ability to remember. As the brain ages, vocabulary may remain strong, but the ability to spot meanings and search for the word you are looking for slows down.

Language puzzles exercise circuits that can help lessen forgetful moments and shorten their duration, but learning cannot become memory without concentration, and without regular maintenance, concentration shrinks with age. These puzzles provide many opportunities for improving and strengthening this important ability and many other useful brain skills:

- Pattern and pathfinding puzzles will strengthen your powers of concentration in the same way that physical exercises build aerobic stamina;

- Logic and memory puzzles will challenge your working memory because you must keep some variables in mind while you test them against others—this frontal-lobe skill is crucial to productive thinking and requires fierce concentration;

- Visual and mechanical puzzles will stretch your visual-spatial mental muscles, which you need to navigate the physical world successfully;

- Divergent-thinking puzzles will encourage your ability to think "outside the box" and see links where others see standard differences—an ability that pays off in any profession;

- Puzzles involving calculation are important to try—even if you are not a numbers person—for they light up many different parts of the brain at once.

Descriptions of the major puzzle types appear on the following pages. The games start on page 8. Good luck!

About the Puzzles

Brain Games for Brain Power is filled with a delightful mix of classic and new puzzle types. To help you get started, here are instructions, tips, and some examples.

WORD GAMES

CROSSWORD PUZZLES

Clues are the deciding factor that determine crossword-solving difficulty. Many solvers mistakenly think strange and unusual words are what make a puzzle challenging. In reality, crossword constructors generally try to avoid grid esoterica, opting for familiar words and expressions.

WORD SUDOKU

The basic sudoku puzzle is a 9 x 9 square grid, split into nine square regions, each containing nine cells. You need to complete the grid so that each row, each column, and each 3 x 3 frame contains the nine letters from the black box above the grid.

There is always a hidden nine-letter word in the diagonal from top left to bottom right.

EXAMPLE

SOLUTION

WORD POWER

These multiple-choice quizzes test your knowledge of grammar and language and help you develop a better vocabulary. Find out where you stand on the Word Power scale by using the simple rating system included on the answer pages.

WORD SEARCHES

In a word search, the challenge is to find hidden words within a grid of letters. Words can be found in vertical columns or horizontal rows or along diagonals, with the letters of the words running either forward or backward.

NUMBER GAMES

SUDOKU

The basic sudoku puzzle is a 9 x 9 square grid, split into nine square regions, each containing nine cells. Complete the grid so that each row, each column, and each 3 x 3 frame contains every number from 1 to 9.

EXAMPLE

SOLUTION

7	4	2	1	6	5	8	9	3
9	3	5	2	4	8	7	6	1
8	6	1	7	3	9	5	2	4
2	1	3	9	5	4	6	8	7
6	5	9	8	7	3	1	4	2
4	7	8	6	1	2	3	5	9
1	8	6	4	9	7	2	3	5
5	2	4	3	8	1	9	7	6
3	9	7	5	2	6	4	1	8

In addition to classic sudoku puzzles, you'll find **SUDOKU X** puzzles, where the main diagonals must include every number from 1 to 9, and **SUDOKU TWINS,** with two overlapping grids.

KAKURO

These puzzles are like crosswords with numbers. There are clues across and down, but the clues are numbers. The solution is a sum that adds up to the clue number.

Each number in a black area is the sum of the numbers that you have to enter in the next empty boxes. The empty boxes that make up the sum are called a run. The sum of the across run is written above the diagonal in the black area, while the sum of the down run is written below the diagonal.

Runs must contain only the numbers 1 through 9, and each number in a run can be used only once. The gray boxes contain only odd numbers; the white contain only even numbers.

EXAMPLE   **SOLUTION**

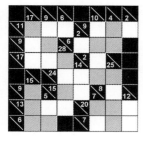

LOGIC PUZZLES

BINAIRO

Binairo puzzles look similar to sudoku puzzles. They are just as simple and challenging, but that is where the similarity ends.

There are two versions: odd and even. The even puzzles feature a 12 x 12 grid. You need to complete the grid with zeros and ones, until there are 6 zeros and 6 ones in every row and every column. No more than two of the same number can be next to or under each other. Rows or columns with exactly the same combination are not allowed.

EXAMPLE   **SOLUTION**

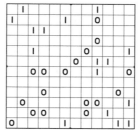

The odd puzzles feature an 11 x 11 grid. You need to complete the grid with zeros and ones until there are 5 zeros and 6 ones in every row and column.

KEEP GOING

In this puzzle, start on a blank square of your choice and connect as many blank squares as possible with one single continuous line.

You can only connect squares along vertical and horizontal lines, not along diagonals. You must continue the connecting line up until the next obstacle—i.e., the rim of the box, a black square, or a square that has already been used.

You can change direction at any obstacle you meet. Each square can be used only once. The number of blank squares left unused is marked in the upper square. There may be more than one solution, but we include only one solution in our answer key.

EXAMPLE   **SOLUTION**

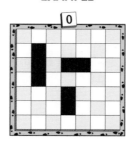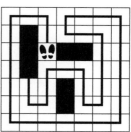

About the Puzzles *(continued)*

NUMBER CLUSTER

Number cluster puzzles are language-free, logical numerical problems. They consist of cubes on a 6 x 6 grid. Numbers have been placed in some of the cubes, while the rest are empty. Your challenge is to complete the grid by creating runs of the same number and length as the number supplied. So where a cube with the number 5 has been included on the grid, you need to create a run of five number 5's, including the cube already shown. The run can be horizontal, vertical, or both horizontal and vertical.

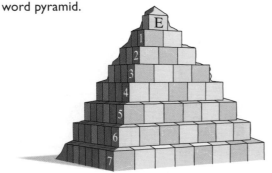

EXAMPLE	SOLUTION

WORD PYRAMID

Each word in the pyramid has the letters of the word above it, plus a new letter.

Using the clues given, answer No.1 and then work your way to the base of the pyramid to complete the word pyramid.

SPORT MAZE

This puzzle is presented on a 6 x 6 grid. Your starting point is indicated by a red cell with a ball and a number. Your objective is to draw the shortest route from the ball to the goal, the only square without a number. You can move only along vertical and horizontal lines, but not along diagonals. The figure on each square indicates the number of squares the ball must be moved in the same direction. You can change direction at each stop.

EXAMPLE	SOLUTION

CAGE THE ANIMALS

This puzzle presents you with a zoo divided into a 16 x 16 grid. The different animals on the grid need to be separated. Draw lines that will completely divide up the grid into smaller squares, with exactly one animal per square.

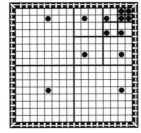

EXAMPLE	SOLUTION

TRIVIA QUIZZES & TRIVIAL PURSUITS

Trivia in a variety of formats and topics will probe the depth of your knowledge of facts. Questions and answers will tempt, tease, and tickle.

Throughout you will find unique mazes, visual conundrums, and other colorful challenges. Each comes with a new name and unique instructions. Our best advice? Patience and perseverance. Your eyes will need time to unravel the visual secrets.

BRAINSNACK® PUZZLES

To solve a BrainSnack® puzzle, you must think logically. You'll need to use one or several strategies to detect direction, differences, and/or similarities, associations, calculations, order, spatial insight, colors, quantities, and distances. A BrainSnack® ensures that all the brain's capacities are fully engaged. These are brain sports at their best!

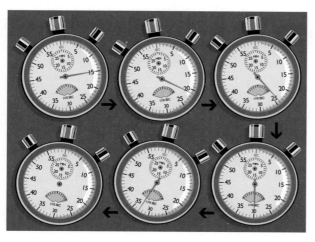

WEATHER CHARTS

We all want to know the weather forecast, and here's your chance to figure it out! Arrows are scattered on a grid. Each arrow points toward a space where a weather symbol should be, but the symbols cannot be next to each other vertically, horizontally, or diagonally. A symbol cannot be placed on top of an arrow. You must determine where the symbols should be placed.

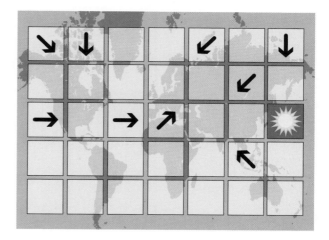

You'll also find short brainteasers scattered throughout these pages. These puzzles will give you a little light relief from the more intense puzzles while still challenging you.

CROSSWORD # Twitter Talk

ACROSS

1. It may be blind
5. Worked hard
11. A psychedelic
14. McGregor in *The Island*
15. Montana capital
16. Ike's WW2 command
17. BR
19. Vietnamese holiday
20. Double duos
21. Coin-op eatery
23. Form of trapshooting
24. Almost never
25. Counting-out word
28. Jacobi in *Gladiator*
29. Liturgical vestment
32. Low hum
34. Tony in *Taxi*
37. Britney Spears song
39. Cottonwood
41. No procrastinator
42. Lieu
44. Richards of the Rolling Stones
46. Like early-morning hours
47. Reacts with enthusiasm
49. ____ off (drives)
51. Buss
53. Hard-____ (hardheaded)
57. Ready for occupancy, to Realtors
59. Air Canada Centre locale
61. Footed vase
62. IMO
64. Bushy do
65. Epoch when mammals emerged
66. Krabappel of *The Simpsons*
67. One or two
68. On the schedule
69. Sit a spell

DOWN

1. Discover balances
2. "Open seven days ____"
3. Discernment
4. Dinner selection
5. Place for tools
6. Millipede features
7. Resembling
8. Aloe ____
9. Last
10. Cowardly sneak
11. LMK
12. Big bargain
13. Loopy
18. Like AAA bonds
22. Attendant of Artemis
26. Org. once headed by Heston
27. Mayonnaise ingredients
28. Call it quits
29. Washboard muscles
30. He ran from Sodom
31. BFN
33. Scots "nix"
35. Scrabble 10-pointer
36. "____ You Ready?"
38. Permanent site
40. Suffix for Capri
43. Tux fronts
45. Literary Nobelist Bergson
48. Carbolic acid
50. Oklahoma resident
51. Cram full
52. Large black-and-white auk
54. Disparaging
55. Berkshire jackets
56. Robert in *Goodbye, Mr. Chips*
58. Village People hit
59. Ring ____
60. Sunday paper page
63. As of now

WORD SEARCH Children

All the words are hidden vertically, horizontally, or diagonally—in both directions. The letters that remain unused form a sentence from left to right.

```
N O I S I V E L E T C H I L D
H O S K C O L B E O D H Y I N
M U S I C H U G L M O R S A E
N B S L I S A A K R E T H V H
M M O L U R I R M V G T O S H
T I T S E C O O O O N M E E F
N L W D O W N C E E A S L X T
E C N S E E S C M H H E A E M
C U T M S I N P T E R M C L E
S A O G D A O U I E L C E F T
E H D A W L O L T P E C S E S
L R D O E Y I H O D B E Y R Y
O T L V W E G B E N B I R C S
D L E E F U U I N F A N T T R
A D R H A I N F L U E N C E O
A N D D L R G S T N E R A P T
P U B D E R N H T W R I T E O
T N E M U G R A T N U O C Y M
```

- ADOLESCENT
- ALLOWANCE
- ARGUMENT
- BLOCKS
- BUILD
- CLIMB
- COUNT
- CYCLE
- DAUGHTER
- DEVELOPMENT
- DISCOVERY
- FIGHT
- HOMEWORK
- HORMONES
- INFANT
- INFLUENCE
- LEARN
- MOTOR SYSTEM
- MOVE
- MUSIC
- PARENTS
- REFLEXES
- SHOELACES
- SKILLS
- SOCIAL
- SWIM
- TELEVISION
- TODDLER
- UNDERAGE
- WRITE
- YOUTH

Word Pyramid

Each word in the pyramid has the letters of the word above it, plus a new letter.

I

(1) The thing
(2) Be seated
(3) Spatter
(4) Dismantle
(5) Clergyman
(6) Buccaneers
(7) Animal that lives in or on a host

CROSSWORD   More Twitter Talk

ACROSS
1 AM or FM specification
5 Warfield of *Night Court*
11 Christian trigram
14 Half a handball game
15 Lets up
16 Just minted
17 HTH
19 Kia compact
20 Cozy contents
21 Big rig, for short
22 Tokyo, prior to 1868
23 River to Kassel
25 Be relevant
27 Like James Monroe's wig
31 Bluish green
32 Paleozoic ___
33 Voting booth feature
35 "Little Orphant Annie" poet
38 Talk out of your head
40 Apollo's isle
42 In play
43 Very, very
45 Took a giant step
47 Wetland
48 Ponderous book
50 Woolgatherers
52 Vanity case
55 Plagued by drought
56 Mu followers
57 Emmy Award depiction
59 Punctuation marks
63 Burn out
64 BRB
66 Cloth measure
67 Renter
68 Curtain color
69 Tierra ___ Fuego
70 Plays to the back row
71 Cassowary cousin

DOWN
1 Thai banknote
2 Winglike petals
3 California wine valley
4 Swooped
5 Was crucial
6 Blood-typing system
7 Shouts while shaking pompoms
8 Hard to climb
9 Bull-riding wear
10 Hopeful one
11 IRL
12 Johanna Spyri heroine
13 Emulate a Justin Bieber fan
18 Alpine warble
24 Whoop it up
26 Westie's wagger
27 Bolivia neighbor
28 Graduate exam
29 WTS
30 Removed text
34 Jet engine sounds
36 It often comes before after
37 Gets a hankering for
39 Run relaxedly
41 Addresses
44 Good-humored
46 Divination deck
49 Revere
51 Party person?
52 All through
53 Trickery
54 Artist's subject
58 Water suspended in air
60 Supersonic number
61 Something to grow on
62 Gull relative
65 "___ whillikers!"

Endings

Endings like **-ism** ("belief"), **-mania** ("obsession"), and **-phobia** ("fear") can tell you a lot about a word's meaning. As you navigate this quiz, pay close attention to the suffix of each term for helpful clues.

. . . .

1. **cryptology** (krip-'tah-luh-jee) *n.*—A: raiding of tombs. B: series of puzzles. C: study of codes.

2. **empathetic** (em-puh-'theh-tik) *adj.*—A: showing understanding or sensitivity. B: sad. C: numb.

3. **ovoid** ('oh-voyd) *adj.*—A: egg-shaped. B: empty. C: passionate.

4. **deify** ('dee-uh-fiy) *v.*—A: treat as a god. B: bring back to life. C: disregard.

5. **perspicacious** (puhr-spuh-'kay-shuhs) *adj.*—A: finicky. B: of acute mental vision. C: fortunate or lucky.

6. **indigenous** (in-'dih-juh-nuhs) *adj.*—A: poor. B: native. C: mixed.

7. **herbicide** ('er-buh-siyd) *n.*—A: greenhouse. B: skin lotion. C: agent used to inhibit or kill plant growth.

8. **pachyderm** ('pa-kih-duhrm) *n.*—A: elephant. B: jellyfish. C: butterfly.

9. **Kafkaesque** (kahf-kuh-'esk) *adj.*—A: nightmarishly complex. B: gigantic. C: left-wing.

10. **atrophy** ('a-truh-fee) *v.*—A: waste away. B: win a prize. C: speak out against.

11. **knavish** ('nay-vish) *adj.*—A: sticky. B: sharply honed. C: deceitful or dishonest.

12. **legalese** (lee-guh-'leez) *n.*—A: passage of laws. B: strict rules. C: legal language.

13. **patriarch** ('pay-tree-ark) *n.*—A: Roman vault. B: father figure. C: homeland.

14. **obsolescent** (ob-soh-'leh-sent) *adj.*—A: teenage. B: quite fat. C: going out of use.

15. **solarium** (soh-'lar-ee-uhm) *n.*—A: sunroom. B: private nook. C: answer to a problem.

Cage the Animals

Draw lines to completely divide up the grid into small squares, with exactly one animal per square. The squares should not overlap.

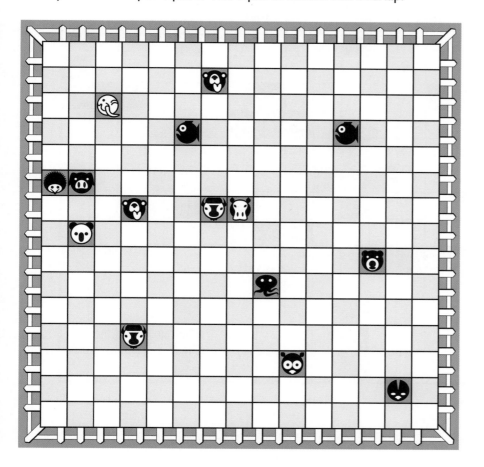

delete**ONE**

Delete one letter from
NOT A SHARK
and rearrange the rest to find a shelter from the storm.

_____

_____

What do the following words have in common?

LAND LONG MOST STRONG QUARTERS LESS

When I Was 17...

ACROSS

1 After-shower powder
5 Corning product
10 Act as accomplice
14 Exchange allowance
15 Steel-collar worker
16 Frog genus
17 Result of a charge
18 Like Rod Serling's stories
19 Weary by excess
20 U.S. Open winner at age 17
23 Liquidate
24 Vehicle for winter fun
25 Gully's big brother
27 WrestleMania locales
31 Fashion designer Saab
32 Discourage
36 Scotch mixer
37 Total
38 Gibson in *The Beaver*
39 Sonoma Valley container
40 Massage target for a runner
42 Pamplona runners
44 Superboy's girlfriend
45 Ritter in *The Misfits*
47 Liam in *Battleship*
49 Prefix for present
51 Widespread confusion
52 Wimbledon winner at age 17
57 Big rig
58 Sam in *Merlin*
59 Solar disk
60 Receipt word
61 Bracelet site
62 Penguins play on one
63 Alan of *M*A*S*H*
64 War-horse
65 Statistics

DOWN

1 Little guys
2 *Permit Me Voyage* author
3 Gabon's capital
4 Exclusive group
5 Like some baking sheets
6 *Camelot* composer
7 Shelter dug into a hillside
8 Dirties
9 Star-spangled
10 Pinball palaces
11 Healing ointment
12 *The Dukes of Hazzard* lawman
13 Scotland's longest river
21 Bread from India
22 Suffix for bombard
25 Jerk the knee
26 To whom a fakir prays
28 Halifax locale
29 Hersey bell town
30 Father of Lies
33 Outback bird
34 ___ Aviv
35 House add-on
41 Snowbird's winter nest
42 Woody Allen film
43 All tied up
44 Fast cat
46 Caesar's 2001
48 Green in *Dark Shadows*
50 ___ *a Letter to My Love* (1981)
51 Berry in *Die Another Day*
52 Time for grace
53 Betwixt
54 Outdoor walk
55 Let off steam
56 "Diana" singer Paul
57 Baden-Baden, e.g.

BRAINSNACK® **Track and Field**

At which point (1–30) will all the runners be next to each other if every runner moves at his indicated speed (number of squares) per unit?

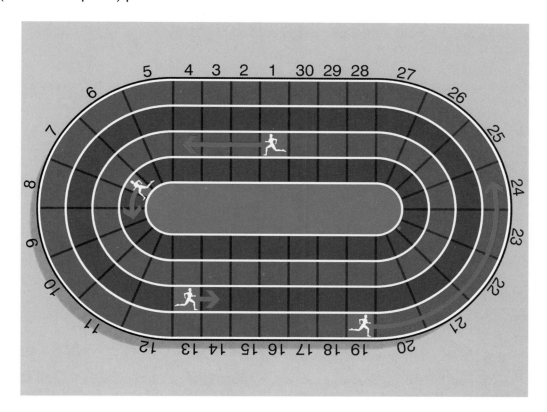

DOUBLETALK

Homophones are words that share the same pronunciation, no matter how they are spelled. If they are spelled differently, then they are called heterographs. Find heterographs meaning:

INVOICED and ASSEMBLE

Bread and Cheese

Bread is perhaps the most universal food on the planet.
And where grains grow well, it's usually ideal land for cattle-grazing.
Hence, cheese-making tends to thrive where diets rely on bread.
Make a meal of these bread-and-cheese questions.

1. What English cheese is known as the "King of cheeses"?

   _____

2. What type of chewy bread is woven into a curly twist and often topped with salt?

   _____

3. Chèvre is made from the milk of what animal?

   _____

4. Roti and puri are breads from what country?

   _____

5. What country produces Manchego cheese?

   _____

6. Where does halloumi cheese come from?

   _____

7. What Italian bread derives its name from its slipperlike shape?

   _____

8. Paneer is a type of cheese from where?

   _____

9. What famous French blue cheese is matured in caves?

   _____

10. Where would you most likely get a farl?

    _____

11. Caerphilly cheese hails from where?

    _____

12. Where does Edam originate from?

    _____

13. What Mexican cheese is soft, unaged fresh cheese made out of pure cow's milk?

    _____

14. What soft-ripened cheese with a snow-white edible rind is most commonly paired with a French baguette?

    _____

Horoscope

Fill in the grid so that every row, every column and every frame of six boxes contains six different symbols: health, work, money, happiness, family and love. Look at the row or column that corresponds with your sign of the zodiac, and find out which of the six symbols are important for you today. The symbols appear in increasing order of importance (1–6). It's up to you to translate the meaning of each symbol to your specific situation.

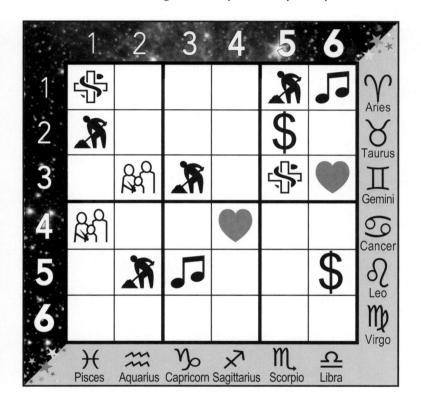

Spot the Differences

Find the nine differences in the image on the bottom right.

trivia

- Who did Grace Kelly marry in 1956?

CROSSWORD · Well Positioned

ACROSS

1 Strumpet
5 Testatrix or aviatrix
10 Harvest yield
14 Busy as ___
15 Defying logic
16 Sign on
17 What headliners get
19 Behold amorously
20 Completely
21 Breathalyzer measure
23 Johnny Reb's org.
24 It's right on the map
25 A Clinton
29 Fun house sounds
32 Douay Bible book
33 Certain stopping point
35 Barbershop sound
36 Lunkhead
37 Popular ISP
38 Stocky antelope
39 Tom Brady's team
41 Kind of sauce or soda
43 Blondie drummer Burke
44 Trains
46 Remote region
48 Walmart rival
49 ___ chi (martial art)
50 Denounce
53 Steakhouse order
57 City in a CCR song
58 Net profit or loss
60 Not windward
61 *The Mystery of ___ Drood*
62 Women's magazine
63 Henry VIII's sixth wife
64 Backsides
65 Pair

DOWN

1 Insulation strip
2 "Peek-___!"
3 Had a bawl
4 Disastrous collapse
5 Fred in *Anchorman*
6 *For Your Eyes ___* (1981)
7 Merry month in Paris
8 "Getting to Know You" singer
9 Fail to fix
10 Gets off the fence
11 One of four in a square
12 Flat plinth, in architecture
13 Banana throwaway
18 Joan's *Judge Dredd* role
22 Scion, for one
25 Basketball
26 Rebecca's husband
27 Southpaw
28 What tree rings represent
29 Large seabird
30 Gold digger
31 Sea foam
34 "The Bells" poet
40 Camp resident
41 Alpinist
42 They're up for discussion
43 Iced
45 Lyric poem
47 Summery
50 Give it up
51 Jabba's slave dancer
52 Point of intersection
53 Recipe directive
54 Needing a shampoo
55 *Lost ___ Mancha* (2002)
56 Exigency
59 "The ___ Corbies"

Sport Maze

Draw the shortest way from the ball to the goal. You can only move along vertical and horizontal lines, not along diagonal lines. The figure on each square indicates the number of squares the ball must be moved in the same direction. You can change direction at each stop.

5	5	5	3	5	2
3	3	1	4	2	5
5	2	1	1	4	5
2	0	0	3	1	1
2	1	1	4	2	
5	2	5	2	1	3

do you KNOW

Who won the 1971 Wimbledon Women's Singles?

ONE LETTER LESS OR MORE

The word on the right side contains the letters of the word on the left side, plus or minus the letter in the middle. One letter is already in the right place.

B A R G A I N S -B ☐ ☐ N ☐ ☐ ☐ ☐

Sudoku

Fill in the grid so that each row, each column, and each 3 x 3 frame contains every number from 1 to 9.

					8			
				1				
		6					5	1
8						9		4
	4		9					
		5	2		4	3		6
	8	2	5		7		3	9
	3	9				6		
7			3	2	9	5		

trivia

• Who founded Max Factor in 1909?

SYMBOL SUMS

Can you work out these number sums using three of these four symbols? + − ÷ ×

33 ☐ 15 ☐ 3 ☐ 6 = 9

Word Wheel

How many words of three or more letters, each including the letter at the center of the wheel, can you make from this diagram? No plurals or conjugations. We've found 19, including one nine-letter word. Can you do better?

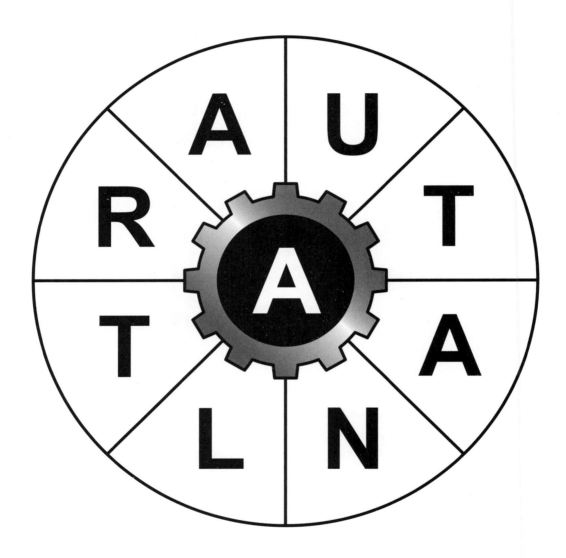

BRAINSNACK® **Ones and Zeros**

The table shows the binary notation of the decimal numbers from 0 to 7. What is the binary notation of the decimal number 12?

```
0000 = 0     0100 = 4
0001 = 1     0101 = 5
0010 = 2     0110 = 6
0011 = 3     0111 = 7

       ? = 12
```

QUICK CROSSWORD

Place the countries listed below in the crossword grid.

CUBA IRAQ BRAZIL FIJI TOGO TONGA LIBYA MALTA FRANCE

Population Groups

All the words are hidden vertically, horizontally, or diagonally—in both directions. The letters that remain unused form a sentence from left to right.

```
C H E R O K E E V I K I N G S
C O M A N C H E M A O P R I I
R S S T I H H E A N E A M S E
E O B I A E I I V R E N O F T
O H A N S C E P S N A M R E G
L E R U A H O I S L I M A T P
E B A I A E A L E K T H A A T
S I E T M N O R S E M E N I N
A C J R S S E U Q S A B H C
P T O A B O R I G I N A L S A
R Y U T V E B B E D O U I N S
E I G A S A R T E D O N E W H
H Z E M R A N S L A L N D S F
S M W H I E E E N I L T L W R
A U O S D E G M S I A E S C A
O V L O E R S S A E W E D B N
Y E U U R R C H E Y E N N E K
O P E A Z S N S A P A C H E S
```

- ABORIGINALS
- APACHES
- ARABS
- ARAMAIC
- BASQUES
- BEDOUINS
- BERBERS
- CHECHENS
- CHEROKEE
- CHEYENNE
- COMANCHE
- CREOLES
- ESKIMOS
- FRANKS
- GERMANS
- INUIT
- JAVANESE
- MAASAI
- MAYA
- MOORS
- NERVII
- NORSEMEN
- PERSIANS
- PYGMIES
- SCOTS
- SHERPA
- TAMILS
- TUAREGS
- VIKINGS
- WALLOONS
- WELSH
- ZULUS

CROSSWORD Spooked

ACROSS

1 *Patriot* ___ (1992)
6 United _____ Emirates
10 Throw for a loop
14 Beaded adders
15 Brand of blocks
16 *Casablanca* croupier
17 Like ballerinas
18 Novi Sad native
19 Sawbucks
20 Slim odds
23 "Am ___ understand ...?"
24 Vince's agent on *Entourage*
25 Seismic sea wave
29 Nike sponsoree
33 Spend time (with)
34 Horse pill
36 Crossed the Channel, à la Ederle
37 Chapel Hill school
38 Glob of gum
39 "Big Blue" company
40 *Alice* diner
42 Old Indian title
44 *For Your Eyes* ___ (1981)
45 Fraser in *The Mummy*
47 Florida fruits
49 MapQuest's owner
50 Computer key
51 Animated arguments
60 Carnegie ___
61 Think-tank product
62 Liquidate
63 Irish Gaelic
64 Straight up, at the bar
65 Wash cycle
66 Unfeeling
67 Sicilian spa
68 Bus coin

DOWN

1 Fiesta
2 "... nine, ten, ___ fat hen"
3 SAT subject
4 Reverberating
5 Seville snooze
6 Likewise
7 Keel scraper
8 India tourist site
9 Charlotte NBA team
10 Particulars
11 Final word
12 Silvery white metal
13 If not
21 Archaeological find
22 Letters for a duke
25 "Under My ___": Rolling Stones
26 Less apt to snap
27 Scrooge McDuck, to Donald
28 Cedar Rapids native
29 TV signal component
30 J.R. of *Dallas*
31 Dining room piece
32 Awards for *Glee*
35 "Well, ___-di-dah"
41 In a tangle
42 Soup cracker
43 Highlands hillside
44 One of the Great Lakes
46 "How ___ Live": LeAnn Rimes
48 Nobelist Camus
51 Give off
52 Whittle down
53 *Casablanca* heroine
54 Heaven on earth
55 James in *East of Eden*
56 *Star Trek: TNG* android
57 Combat vehicle
58 In ___ (actually)
59 Watched

Number Fun 1

Every calculation contains a +, −, and x. The number in each blue square is the total of the four numbers at each of its corners. Can you fill in the grid?

4		1		11		1	=	54
	10		20		30			
3							=	84
	40		50		60			
17							=	198
	70		80		90			
4							=	90
=		=		=		=		
72		23		49		35		

do you KNOW?

Which artist painted "The Kiss" and "Danaë"?

DOODLE PUZZLE

A doodle puzzle is a combination of images, letters, and/or numbers that represent a word or a concept. If you cannot solve a doodle puzzle, do not look at the answer right away. Think hard—and outside the box.

Word Sudoku

Complete the grid so that each row, each column, and each 3 x 3 frame contains the nine letters from the black box below. The hidden nine-letter word is in the diagonal from top left to bottom right.

A B D G I N R S T

G	N	T	I			S		A
D		S			N	B		I
		I				G	N	
T	D		N					
			T	D		A	B	
	B				I		R	
S				T				
		D			S	R		
		A						

trivia

- Who is the youngest winner of an Oscar?

_____

UNCANNY TURN

Rearrange the letters of the phrase below to form a cognate anagram, one that is related or connected in meaning to the original phrase. The answer can be one or more words.

SEE APART

Oaters

ACROSS

1 Harmon of *NCIS*
5 Crushed fabric
10 Prewedding party
14 North African seaport
15 Become weatherworn
16 Pitch
17 1992 Clint Eastwood film
19 Giant slain by Odin
20 Hollywood acting family
21 Trip
23 Scrunch up
24 2011 Jay-Z/Kanye West song
25 Observed
27 Said "Hi"
30 "___ that happen?
33 1992 French Open winner
35 Foot part
36 Wallach in *The Magnificent Seven*
37 Guitarist Paul
38 Bulls' org.
39 Lunar valley
41 Lipstick type
43 Spree
44 Brazil neighbor
46 Needle reaction
48 Hard up
49 Burrowing rodent
53 Walter in *The Westerner*
56 Question the integrity of
57 Front-rank
58 1948 John Wayne film
60 Nine-digit IDs
61 Hatrack setting
62 "___ bien!"
63 "Superwoman" singer Alicia
64 Adversary
65 Miffed

DOWN

1 React to a loss
2 Golf great Palmer
3 Travels like Huck
4 Gnarled
5 College conferrals
6 Apple of Discord thrower
7 Penultimate month: Abbr.
8 Fateful March date
9 Wise advisers
10 Thwarts
11 Site of the O.K. Corral
12 Blue dye
13 Richard in *Chicago*
18 Have confidence in
22 SUV
26 "The Gift of the Magi" heroine
27 Bas-relief material
28 Isle near Corsica
29 Expensive
30 Coriander, e.g.
31 Mishmash
32 1968 Charlton Heston film
34 Zodiac member
40 Pride Lands female
41 Tallest animal
42 Synopsis
43 Ultimatums
45 Paul ___ Hindenburg
47 Andy of the comics
50 Close-up lens
51 Yellow brown
52 This and that
53 Catch some rays
54 Hybrid tea
55 When shadows are short
56 Gossip's subject
59 Bread choice

Hourglass

Starting in the middle, each word in the top half has the letters of the word below it, plus a new letter, and each word in the bottom half has the letters of the word above it, plus a new letter.

(1) Mysteries
(2) Figures
(3) Competitions
(4) Very large
(5) Passageway
(6) Broker
(7) Feeding
(8) Wine

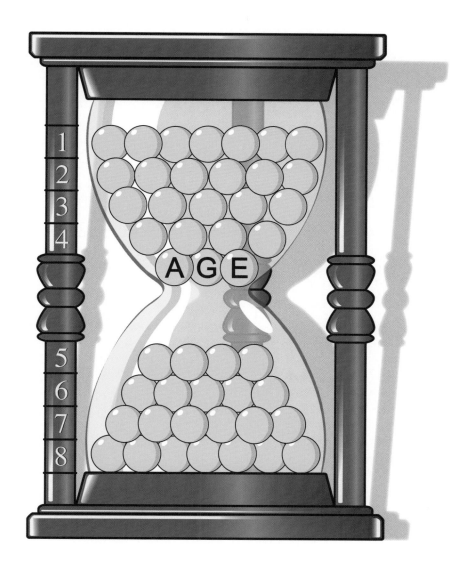

Where will the sun shine? With the knowledge that each arrow points to a place where a symbol should be, can you locate the sunny spots? The symbols cannot be next to each other vertically, horizontally, or diagonally. A symbol cannot be placed on top of an arrow. We show one symbol.

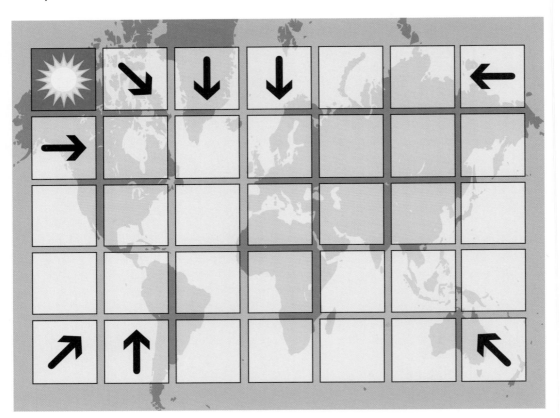

TRIANAGRAM

Three-word groups of anagrams are also called triplets or trianagrams.
Complete the group:

S L A T H E R _ _ _ _ _ _ _   _ _ _ _ _ _ _

CROSSWORD Horse Operas

ACROSS

1 Make fast
5 Kelly in *Chaplin*
10 Prickly heat, e.g.
14 Ancient Peruvian
15 Anchor position
16 Electric sword
17 1939 John Wayne film
19 Imitative one
20 Racetrack margins of victory
21 Netherlands
23 San Simeon, e.g.
24 "Be" singer Diamond
25 "Drat!"
27 Bend out of shape
30 "___ Indigo"
33 Moral philosophy
35 Cellist Ma
36 Cleo's pet
37 German article
38 *Exodus* actor Mineo
39 Golf course designer Jones
41 Blu in *Rio*, for one
43 Wind down
44 New York City park
46 Good enough to eat
48 Deeply focused
49 "Inside Out" singer Yearwood
53 Quotes alternative
56 Riddles
57 Where to get some ice time
58 1968 Clint Eastwood film
60 Ford SUV
61 Inventor Howe
62 "Waiting for the Robert ___"
63 Progeny
64 Excites, slangily
65 Family rooms

DOWN

1 Hosiery yarn
2 Sweetens the kitty
3 Meager
4 Merle of Nashville
5 Sugar harvester's tool
6 Native Oklahomans
7 Lyricist Gershwin
8 Like cheesecake
9 Mouthed but not spoken
10 *Dogs in the City* genre
11 2008 Viggo Mortensen film
12 Visible
13 Bunch of cattle
18 "Trust in Me" singer James
22 ___ *Misérables*
26 Pick pockets
27 Kuwaiti coin
28 Reynolds in *Green Lantern*
29 Enameled ware
30 Golfer Leishman
31 Hosea, in the Douay
32 2003 Kevin Costner film
34 "How Dry I Am" syllable
40 Tailed creepily
41 Corresponds exactly
42 Testimony giver
43 Tipped the scales
45 Upstate NY college
47 Prudish
50 Amused look
51 Duvall's *Godfather* role
52 Bonfire remains
53 Piques
54 Driftwood carrier
55 Red-tag event
56 "Omigosh!"
59 *Delta of Venus* author

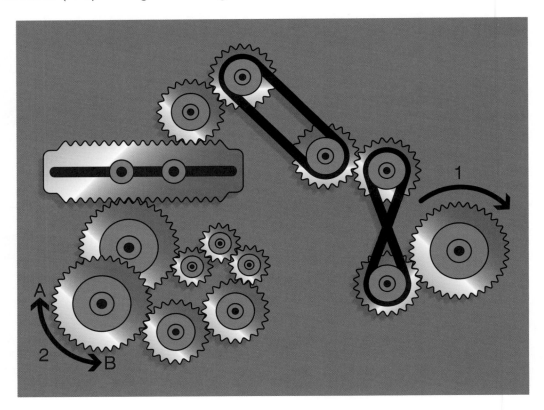

Which direction (A–B) will cog 2 turn if cog 1 turns clockwise?

DOODLE PUZZLE

A doodle puzzle is a combination of images, letters, and/or numbers that represent a word or a concept. If you cannot solve a doodle puzzle, do not look at the answer right away. Think hard—and outside the box.

TRIVIA QUIZ # A Quick Dip

How well do you know your pool lingo?
Can you enter into this round with hardly a splash, or do you prefer to do cannonballs?

1. What name is given to the final swimmer in a relay race?

   a. Anchor
   b. Alternate
   c. Steamer

2. The starting spot behind each lane is known as what?

   a. Slab
   b. Chop
   c. Block

3. The area along the edge of the pool where water overflows and recirculates is called:

   a. Lane
   b. Gutter
   c. Alley

4. The wave created in front of the swimmer's head as they move through the water is called a:

   a. Bow wave
   b. Hurdle wave
   c. Crest wave

5. Which competitive stroke incorporates a dolphin kick?

   a. Freestyle
   b. Breaststroke
   c. Butterfly

6. What term describes a race or event held in a lake or ocean?

   a. Long-distance swimming
   b. Cross-channel swimming
   c. Open-body swimming

7. What term describes a swimmer who is swimming facedown on his or her stomach?

   a. Deft
   b. Prone
   c. Agile

8. Once their qualifying times are determined, in which lanes are the fastest swimmers placed in a pool?

   a. Outside lanes
   b. Center lanes
   c. They're positioned right-to-left

9. What is it called when a swimmer kicks the legs independently of each other, not in unison, in an up-and-down motion?

   a. Spring kick
   b. Flutter kick
   c. Dolphin kick

10. The resistance the water causes swimmers as they move through the water is known as:

    a. Draw
    b. Heave
    c. Drag

Theater

All the words are hidden vertically, horizontally, or diagonally—in both directions. The letters that remain unused form a sentence from left to right.

```
A M T Y P E C A S T I N G A E
U O T T E R B I L A S I C C P
A P P L A U S E P A M T L I U
R I O H C S C A P E O A L A O
Y K T R A G E D Y R P T R H R
A E T Y E U N S E S E A C D T
C E L A S R A E H E R M A O Y
E R M L U M R B I N A A S T A
C G Y P O C I I O K N O T F L
N P S W H O O P E L A Y I Y P
E R T O Y M A U C T I N N T E
I O E D A E P G N I T H G I L
D M R A L D I R E C T O R L C
U P Y H P Y O I D U T S G A A
A T P S S A M A T E U R O R R
N E L N O O F F U B G M U O I
S R A I C A N D W I N G S M M
D A Y P A N T O M I M E N C E
```

- ACTOR
- AMATEUR
- APPLAUSE
- AUDIENCE
- BUFFOON
- CASTING
- CHOIR
- COMEDY
- DIRECTOR
- DRAMA
- EPIC
- GREEK
- LIBRETTO
- LIGHTING
- MAKE-UP
- MIRACLE PLAY
- MORALITY
- MYSTERY PLAY
- OPERA
- PANTOMIME
- PLAYHOUSE
- PROMPTER
- REHEARSAL
- SCENARIO
- SHADOW PLAY
- STUDIO
- TRAGEDY
- TROUPE
- TYPECASTING
- WINGS

Kakuro

Each number in a black area is the sum of the numbers that you have to enter in the next empty boxes. The empty boxes that make up the sum are called a run. The sum of the across run is written above the diagonal in the black area, and the sum of the down run is written below the diagonal. Runs can only contain the numbers 1 through 9, and each number in a run can only be used once. The gray boxes only contain odd numbers and the white only even numbers.

trivia

- Who is Sherlock Holmes's nemesis?

CROSSWORD — Horse and Rider

ACROSS

1 One of the Marx Brothers
6 *Little Women* sister
10 Charades craft
14 Every seventh day
15 1975 Wimbledon winner
16 Biblical lyre
17 Zoo noises
18 Word with "fried" or "crazy"
19 Pall
20 2012 Kentucky Derby winner
23 French donkey
24 Carp relative
25 First American in space
29 Rather than
33 ___ d'oeuvre
34 One who cries "Uncle!"
36 Fashion monthly
37 Email address suffix
38 ___-jongg
39 Out of sorts
40 First grandchild
42 Brown of song
44 Neil Young protest song
45 Reconciles
47 Heroic deeds
49 "Y" pluralized
50 Pinky-out drink
51 Jockey on 20-Across
59 Raymond of *Ironside*
60 Broadway award
61 Colander
62 "In ___ of flowers ..."
63 *Aquarius* musical
64 Queen ___ lace
65 Pitfall
66 Kruger in *High Noon*
67 It gets belted around

DOWN

1 Mata of espionage
2 Military truant
3 Not illusory
4 Conceivably
5 Figure skater Baiul
6 Military installation
7 "Se Me ___ Escapando": ABBA
8 Hardly heavy
9 Emma or Jane Eyre, e.g.
10 Rainforest blade
11 "... here on Gilligan's ___"
12 Secure a blimp
13 Suffix with cook or rook
21 *Deserving Design* designer Yip
22 QB stats
25 Pumps and flats
26 "Stormy Weather" singer Lena
27 Cereal fungus
28 Coins in a $5 roll
29 Blood of the gods
30 Judge Smails in *Caddyshack*
31 Kate's sitcom partner
32 Birthplace of Apollo
35 Auditory organ
41 35-Down bone
42 Monarchy within South Africa
43 Cousin of Bigfoot
44 Musical "sweet potato"
46 Maui neckwear
48 Playground plank
51 Sierra Club founder
52 Surroundings
53 Zodiac animal
54 Module
55 Hardly a veteran
56 Santoni in *Dirty Harry*
57 Special nights
58 Pungency
59 Sandwich order

Number Cluster

Cubes showing numbers have been placed on the grid below, with some spaces left empty. Can you complete the grid by creating runs of the same number and of the same length as the number? So, where a cube with number 5 has been included on the grid, you need to create a run of five number 5's, including the cube already shown. The run can be horizontal, vertical, or both horizontal and vertical.

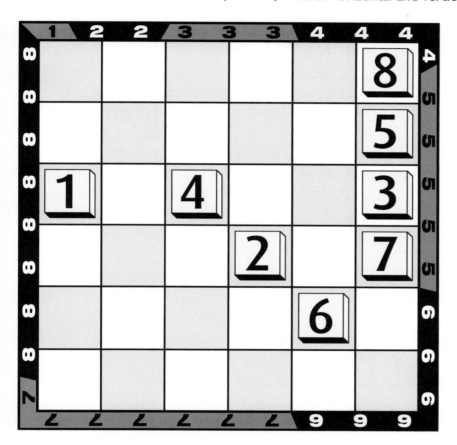

SANDWICH

What four-letter word belongs between the word at left and the word at right, so that the first and second word, and the second and third word, each form a common compound word or phrase?

O V E R _ _ _ _ L E S S

Sudoku X

Fill in the grid so that each row, each column, and each 3 × 3 frame contains every number from 1 to 9. The two main diagonals of the grid also contain every number from 1 to 9.

		1						
	7			3	5	1		
								8
3		6		7	1			
				5	9	3	2	6
9	8		6	2	3	7		
4		7	3	1		8		
		3						7
					7	5	3	

do you KNOW

Who composed *Tosca?*

BLOCK ANAGRAM

Form the word that is described in the parentheses using the letters above the grid. Extra letters are already in the right place.

ACHILLES (2012 Olympic gold medal men's 110-m butterfly)

M		H	E			P			P	

CROSSWORD **Bond Baddies**

ACROSS
1 Schussboomer's lift
5 List for honor students
10 Doctrines
14 *The Puritans* novelist Bates
15 "Hands down" is one
16 Campus sports org.
17 *Skyfall* villain
19 Like cooking apples
20 Former
21 Tour de France winner Contador
23 "___ Had a Hammer"
24 Pre-euro Italian coin
25 *The ___ of King George* (1994)
29 Math point
32 Monster of fiction
33 Fab Four member
35 Landlocked African nation
36 ___ Mahal
37 Momentous time period
38 *Children of the Albatross* author
39 Birds from green eggs
41 Judi in *Casino Royale*
43 *CIA Diary* author
44 Counted up
46 City near San Francisco
48 Fleming and McEwan
49 Dixie soldier
50 Synod
53 Standoff
57 Relax
58 Bond villain played by Gert Fröbe
60 Mrs. Shakespeare
61 "Oh, ___ don't!"
62 Roman road
63 Cherry, e.g.
64 Period of time
65 Pumps for info

DOWN
1 Source of poi
2 Healthy cereal
3 Emollient source
4 Comedian's shtick
5 Fire
6 Falco in *The Sopranos*
7 Distress
8 Spectacular star
9 What Alice became
10 The time being
11 *The Man with the Golden Gun* villain
12 Store
13 Hoshi of *Star Trek: Enterprise*
18 Milton Bradley board game
22 Paper Mate rival
25 Sacred song
26 Blue-headed lizard
27 Bond villain played by Joseph Wiseman
28 Sleipnir, for Odin
29 Malfoy of Hogwarts School
30 Not of this world
31 Added fiberfill
34 Prince Valiant's son
40 Biased
41 Drawing-board output
42 Deleterious
43 Balkan state
45 LLC relative
47 De Gaulle's hat
50 Avian stomach
51 Wine prefix
52 Skating figure
53 Screen favorite
54 NCO Club members: Abbr.
55 Probe for
56 Makes mistakes
59 Caustic alkaline

Good Hand?

Which playing card (A–D) from the same deck is the only suitable replacement for the question mark?

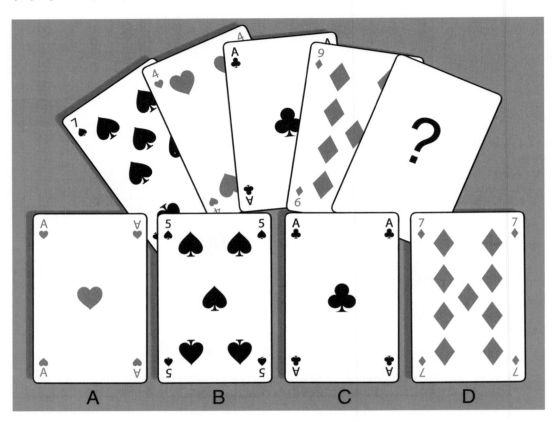

LETTER LINE

Put a letter in each of the squares below to make a word that is pretty basic.
The number clues refer to other words that can be made from the whole.

9 1 8 2 4 KINGDOM • 1 6 8 4 1 2 A KIND OF PAINT • 10 5 6 CURRENCY
2 8 4 1 6 7 REGRET, EXPRESS SORROW • 7 8 4 5 2 10 SHEEPISHLY

1	2	3	4	5	6	7	8	9	10

WORD POWER   Construction & Tools

Do you know your adze from your auger? And what exactly is a grommet? Sharpen your verbal edge by mastering these words related to construction and tools.

. . . .

1. **serrated** ('seh-ray-ted) *adj.*— A: primed for painting. B: toothed like a saw. C: waterproof.

2. **vise** (viys) *n.*—A: clamp that holds an object in place. B: mechanism to lift a car. C: flaw in building materials.

3. **adze** (adz) *n.*—A: ax-like tool with a curved blade. B: small rubber mallet. C: piece of scrap wood.

4. **flanged** (flanjd) *adj.*—A: sealed with wax. B: with a protruding rim. C: wound tightly.

5. **torque** (tork) *n.*—A: twisting force. B: mechanical failure. C: electrical current.

6. **auger** ('ah-ger) *n.*—A: master woodworker. B: spiral drill bit. C: sailor's knife.

7. **dowel** (dowl) *n.*—A: toilet plunger. B: peg. C: paint roller.

8. **ferrule** ('ferr-uhl) *n.*— A: beveled edge. B: tape measure. C: protective cap.

9. **cambered** ('kam-berd) *adj.*—A: encircled. B: arched. C: stained.

10. **gauge** (gayj) *n.*—A: deep groove. B: plumber's wrench. C: measuring instrument.

11. **loupe** (loop) *n.*—A: cutter. B: gripper. C: magnifier.

12. **awl** (all) *n.*—A: pointed tool for piercing holes. B: large wheelbarrow. C: system of pulleys.

13. **casters** ('kass-terz) *n.*— A: swiveling wheels. B: ball bearings. C: fishing reels.

14. **grommet** ('grah-meht) *n.*— A: ring that reinforces. B: copper pipe. C: gutter.

15. **kludge** (klooj) *n.*—A: blueprint. B: makeshift solution. C: tangled wire.

CROSSWORD — Arf!

ACROSS

1 Bashful, e.g.
6 Club in a Manilow song
10 Muppet saxophonist
14 Edmonton skater
15 Humdinger
16 Girl-watch
17 Russian lake
18 Maple genus
19 Ishii of *Kill Bill* films
20 Dog held sacred by the Aztecs
23 Clod
24 Dove sound
25 Deny
29 Classily clad
33 Intelligence
34 See the old gang
36 "You said it!"
37 Sky altar
38 Gardner in *On the Beach*
39 Peter Ustinov's title
40 Stand up
42 Parcel
44 Mouse cousin
45 Front-runners
47 Trudge
49 "___ little teapot ..."
50 Inner city
51 "Monopoly" token
60 *Othello* ensign
61 Thailand neighbor
62 Ahead of time
63 Eye suggestively
64 "Orinoco Flow" singer
65 Wood finish
66 Canadian loonies
67 Letter opener
68 Uptight

DOWN

1 Destine to oblivion
2 Oenophile's drink of choice
3 Ovechkin of hockey
4 Areas
5 Slugfest
6 Highland group
7 "That smarts!"
8 Something to cop
9 Outer part of the ear
10 Animal science
11 Fairy-tale heavy
12 Corrida cheers
13 Perfect scores
21 At a distance
22 Red deer
25 Twist into a knotted form
26 Hawk home
27 *When ___ Kid* (Bill Cosby album)
28 *Seven ___ in Tibet* (1997)
29 Legislate
30 Ancient storyteller
31 They grow on you
32 Babe Ruth's number
35 Tanning ray
41 Masthead names
42 Was behind
43 Quiz answer
44 iPhone mode
46 911 responder
48 Put a stop to
51 Storage tower
52 Normandy city
53 Vaulted arch
54 All there
55 Georgetown mascot
56 Romanov ruler
57 Mideast land
58 New Haven team
59 Sandberg of baseball

Sport Maze

Draw the shortest way from the ball to the goal. You can only move along vertical and horizontal lines, not along diagonal lines. The figure on each square indicates the number of squares the ball must be moved in the same direction. You can change direction at each stop.

3	1	4	5	5	1
3	4	1	3	3	5
3	3	1	1	0	1
3	3	1	1	4	5
5	2	3	3		5
2	2	3	5	4	5

do you KNOW?

Who hosted the 1992 Winter Olympics?

_____

_____

ONE LETTER LESS OR MORE

The word on the right side contains the letters of the word on the left side, plus or minus the letter in the middle. One letter is already in the right place.

| H | A | R | D | W | A | R | E | -R- | | | H | | | |

Flavors

All the words are hidden vertically, horizontally, or diagonally—in both directions. The letters that remain unused form a sentence from left to right.

```
S A F L A V M L A B N O M E L
A O E C A M R E C C O M N H I
F P A R S L E Y L E U N A N S
F C A R D A M O M S L L I D A
R C S O N E V O T R I E S O B
O A E S O E S A N P P Y R I N
N T S E G C R R Y D R O E Y O
R L A M A D A N E R A S P D D
T A M A R I N D E G R I A P T
G S E R R D I B Y V N U E G Y
A E T Y A E R T C R H I C A E
T L M A T E C H C H O E G N T
U B L T P S A Y T S E V I H C
E A S I U I T M H E N R A A T
U T N R N N A E L F L A V S V
C U M I N A O N O M A N N I C
J R O F A D V A L E R I A N L
I S H F E N N E L G A R L I C
```

- ALMOND
- ANISEED
- BASIL
- CARDAMOM
- CELERY
- CHERVIL
- CHIVES
- CINNAMON
- CLOVE
- CUMIN
- CURRY
- DILL
- FENNEL
- GARLIC
- GINGER
- JUNIPER BERRY
- LEMON BALM
- MACE
- MUSTARD
- NUTMEG
- ONION
- PARSLEY
- POPPY
- ROSEMARY
- SAFFRON
- SAGE
- SAVORY
- SESAME
- TABLE SALT
- TAMARIND
- TARRAGON
- THYME
- VALERIAN
- VANILLA

Cage the Animals

Draw lines to completely divide up the grid into small squares, with
exactly one animal per square. The squares should not overlap.

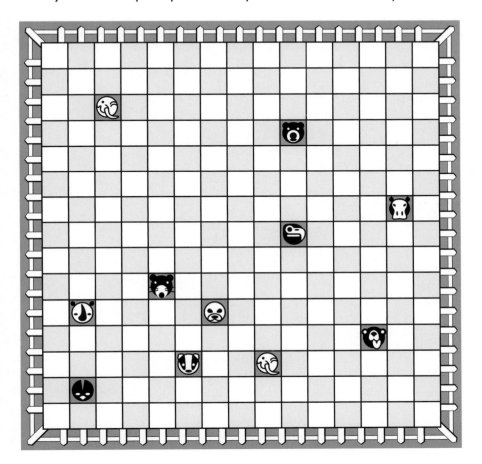

FRIENDS

What do the following words have in common?

LORD BLED CRAFT DEN HORSE LOCK

If you look only at the shape of the letters, which letter block should replace the question mark?

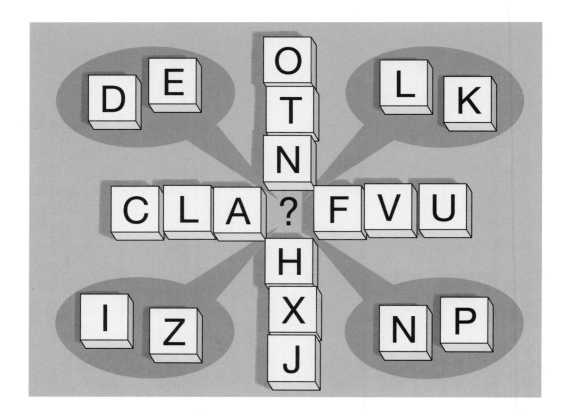

DOODLE PUZZLE

A doodle puzzle is a combination of images, letters, and/or numbers that represent a word or a concept. If you cannot solve a doodle puzzle, do not look at the answer right away. Think hard—and outside the box.

TIKA-**TIKA**
TOO
♪ **TI-TI** ♫
TA **TA**

CROSSWORD # Avian Look-alikes

ACROSS

1 Zodiacal border
5 Drench, as a fire
10 Gossip page couple
14 *The Thin Man* dog
15 Put down the hatch
16 Army mascot
17 Tiniest complaint
18 Jousting horse
19 Mythic Hun
20 Emu look-alike
22 Great auk look-alike
24 Suffix for cyan
25 Ben Canaan of *Exodus*
26 Signals invitingly
30 Explorer Drake
34 Logan of *60 Minutes*
35 Apollo's isle of birth
37 90° from north
38 Strain ___ gnat
39 "You Will Be My ___
   True Love"
40 Figure skater Asada
41 Chan's were numbered
43 Wedding-cake figure
45 Lute-shaped fruit
46 Adversaries
48 Open
50 British isle
51 "___ for Two"
52 Swift look-alike
56 Wood stork look-alike
60 *Guys and Dolls* doll
61 Consumer crusader
   Ralph
63 What a stitch saves
64 Sandusky's lake
65 Jalopy
66 Secular
67 Wild carrot, e.g.
68 Stopped
69 "Sunny" egg part

DOWN

1 Mob chief
2 Utilizes
3 Let it be, on a proof
4 Red spice
5 Drop
6 Imprecation
7 Sun-dance tribe
8 Slowly flow
9 Charms
10 John Lennon song
11 *The Nutcracker* costume
12 She outwrestled Thor
13 "Kiss ___ the Rain":
   Streisand

21 "All ___ Is Dream of
   You"
23 Ted Nugent's org.
26 Apathetic
27 Shirley in *Goldfinger*
28 Great blue heron look-
   alike
29 Kenmore's company
30 Cheesy Swiss dish
31 Minor role
32 *I, Robot* author Asimov
33 Great egret look-alike
36 Half of CIV
42 Got a whiff of
43 "If I Were a Boy" singer

44 Became a member
45 How the Amish dress
47 Not up to snuff
49 Chevrolet ___ Air
52 Goldeneye look-alike
53 Sported
54 Shepard's ___ *of
   the Mind*
55 Sound the alert
56 Ex-Beatle Best
57 "So long, Giorgio!"
58 Blue dye
59 Giraffe feature

Face Value

Which number should replace the question mark?

QUICK WORD SEARCH

Find the stones or gems listed below in the word search grid.

K	Y	A	N	I	T	E	H	T	N	I	C	A	J	Y
L	E	I	F	I	T	E	T	I	T	A	M	E	H	R
A	M	B	E	R	I	H	P	P	A	S	D	Q	U	O
E	T	A	G	A	D	I	A	M	O	N	D	B	F	V
Z	A	P	O	T	O	D	I	R	E	P	Y	J	Z	I

**AGATE AMBER DIAMOND HEMATITE IVORY JACINTH
KYANITE LEIFITE PERIDOT RUBY SAPPHIRE TOPAZ**

Kakuro

Each number in a black area is the sum of the numbers that you have to enter in the next empty boxes. The empty boxes that make up the sum are called a run. The sum of the across run is written above the diagonal in the black area, and the sum of the down run is written below the diagonal. Runs can only contain the numbers 1 through 9, and each number in a run can only be used once. The gray boxes only contain odd numbers and the white only even numbers.

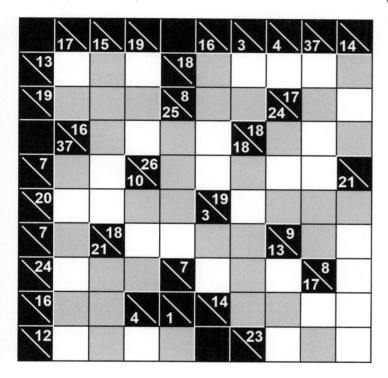

trivia

- Who created *The Simpsons*?

Winning Hands

ACROSS

1 Henhouse
5 Rose distillation
10 Not a done deal
14 "Natural" hairstyle
15 Kickapoos, e.g.
16 Slipper
17 Frehley and Ventura
19 Emotional appeal
20 Vanity affair
21 Acting as guardian
23 Naysayer
24 Number crunching
25 Amount to pay
27 Lacking a sound basis
30 "Hold ___ your hat!"
33 Held a watch on
35 "You bet!"
36 Unrefined
37 Small fry
38 Tessio in *The Godfather*
39 Riding whip
41 Babar's daughter
43 Stephen King novel
44 Take over
46 Utah ski resort
48 ___-date (current)
49 Previous
53 "The First Cut Is the ___": Rod Stewart
56 Cliché
57 "Tell me ___ haven't heard"
58 The Magi
60 Mrs. Shakespeare
61 Relaxed
62 In place, in a way
63 Fresh talk
64 "Same here!"
65 Shows fallibility

DOWN

1 Dressed like Batman
2 Coming-___ story
3 Constellation east of Taurus
4 Greek architecture feature
5 In the beginning
6 Fairway feature
7 First of three-in-a-row
8 Connive with a con
9 Picked up the thread
10 Driving force
11 It's heaven to angels
12 Alpert's "Spanish ___"
13 Sentence period
18 Crossword cookie
22 *The Joy Luck Club* author
26 Property paper
27 Aquarium fish
28 Orenburg's river
29 Make like a bear
30 Ocean killer
31 Meth lab raider
32 Elizabeth and Victoria
34 Bossy's sound
40 Critters in litters
41 Like some brownies
42 Fettuccine sauce
43 Purplish-red
45 Rock suffix
47 Borrowed without permission
50 Forty-niner
51 Mystery Writers award
52 Takes a break
53 "When in Rome, ___ the Romans ..."
54 Sicilian spa
55 The talk of Bangkok
56 Red veggie
59 Trio in front of U

Keep Going

Start on a blank square of your choice and connect as many blank squares as possible with one single continuous line. You can only connect squares along vertical and horizontal lines, not along diagonal lines. You must continue the connecting lineup until the next obstacle, i.e., the border of the box, a black square, or a square that has already been used. You can change direction at any obstacle you meet. Each square can only be used once. The number of blank squares that will be left unused is marked in the upper square. There is more than one solution. We only show one solution.

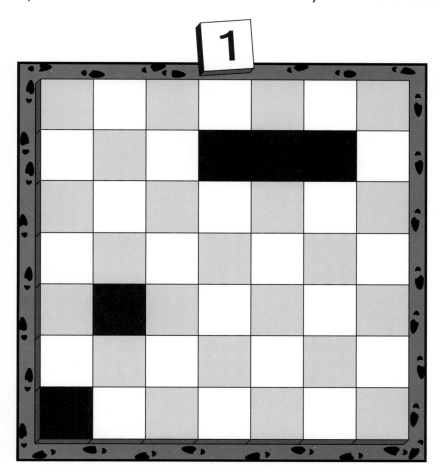

Noah's Ark

Loading them up two-by-two was probably the easy part. Consider all the other intricacies involved in the animal kingdom and see how you would fare in Noah's shoes.

1. What is the largest species of penguin?

   _____

2. What is the name of the shelter a hedgehog builds to live in through the winter?

   _____

3. What is the name of the fungal delicacy sought out by pigs?

   _____

4. According to folklore, what does it mean when swallows are flying high?

   _____

5. Is a thorny devil a reptile or an insect?

   _____

6. What is the name of the repellant acid produced by ants?

   _____

7. What is the main food of salmon, which gives them their pink-tinted flesh?

   _____

8. What is the common name for the egg cases of skates and rays, which are often found washed up on beaches?

   _____

9. Which ancient people actually ate the edible dormouse and considered it a delicacy?

   _____

10. What color is the skin of a polar bear?

    _____

11. What is the name of the world's heaviest insect?

    _____

12. After the two species of elephant, what is the next largest land mammal?

    _____

13. What is the slowest animal in the world?

    _____

14. What the longest living mammal on Earth?

    _____

Fore!

This is a tricky hole at The Masters, with bunkers and water hazards and long grass. If you can get from the tee to the flag without encountering a hazard, you have a Hole in One and are well on your way to being a champion. There is only one route to the pin that avoids the hazards. Each time you pass through a bunker, a water hazard, or long grass, you drop a shot. If you pass through one bunker, your score when you reach the flag is 2. If you encounter two bunkers and a water hazard, your score is 4 and maybe this game is just not for you! The solution shows the Hole in One pathway.

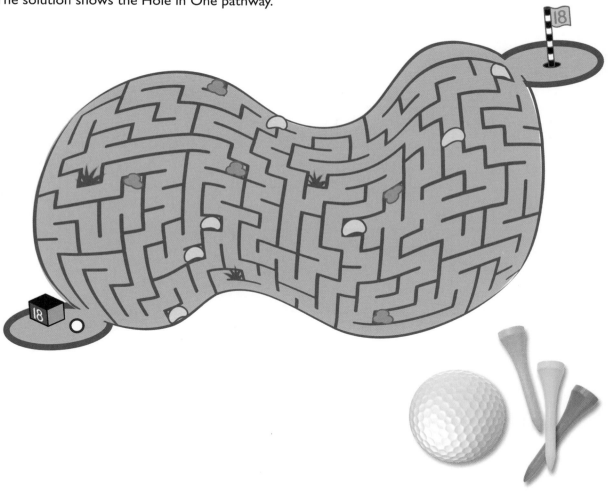

Word Sudoku

Complete the grid so that each row, each column, and each 3 x 3 frame contains the nine letters from the black box below. The hidden nine-letter word is in the diagonal from top left to bottom right.

B E I M O P R T V

			T			B		
V	R	O				T		
	T	I				E		V
I	B	V	M			O		
T					V			
M			O	P				
E	V			O	P			B
O			E		R	V		
			T	B				E

do you KNOW

What is the architectural style of the White House?

UNCANNY TURN

Rearrange the letters of the phrase below to form a cognate anagram, one that is related or connected in meaning to the original phrase. The answer can be one or more words.

GUN HINT

CROSSWORD Tiny Tots

ACROSS
1 Tuba's pitch
5 Lowlife
10 Alternative to a chairlift
14 Helm position
15 Seven ___ of Rome
16 Kin of a wheeze
17 Ty Warner collectible
19 Final farewell of a sort
20 Valuable weasels
21 Altar server
23 Stiletto
24 Seed cover
25 Time periods of note
27 Fellowship
30 Inconsequential lie
33 Taking the wrong way?
35 Introductory word
36 It's split at CERN
38 Sandwich wrap
40 Menu fish
41 Kidney-connected
43 *Air Music* composer
45 "___ Blues": Beatles
46 Like a crow's call
48 Sedona and Sorento
50 Steer clear of
51 "Look at Me, I'm Sandra Dee" musical
55 ___ for Humanity
58 Party
59 Esfahan locale
60 Gen Xer's parent, maybe
62 Scoff
63 Colombian plain
64 Great review
65 Robert in *Airplane!*
66 Senior
67 *Without ___* (Grateful Dead album)

DOWN
1 Toddlers
2 On one's toes
3 Shabby
4 Senescent
5 Swiftest cats
6 Barbecue favorite
7 She, in Sao Paulo
8 Napoleon's isle
9 1960 Hitchcock film
10 Streetcars
11 *It's a Gift* star
12 Came to rest
13 Network of nerves
18 Like neon
22 "Yow!"
26 Anchor store at many malls
27 Tony ___ (Iron Man)
28 Prefix for gram
29 River into North Sea
30 Jamie of *M*A*S*H*
31 Virginia willow
32 Teen with a major-league contract
34 To's partner
37 Autocratic political orgs.
39 Kramer, to Seinfeld
42 Dolt
44 Hockey great Lemieux
47 Lacking know-how
49 Flamenco dancer, often
52 Clio contender
53 Food strainer
54 Long-legged bird
55 On cloud nine
56 Prima donna's song
57 Like John Isner
58 "... for auld lang ___"
61 Good, in slang

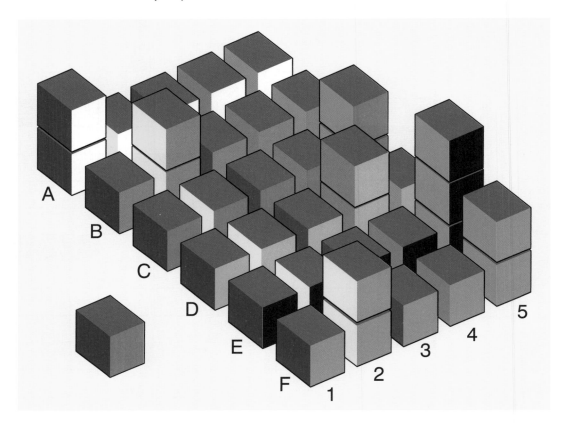

BRAINSNACK® Cube Location

On which coordinates should you place the detached cube? Answer like this: B4.

DOUBLETALK

Homophones are words that share the same pronunciation, no matter how they are spelled. If they are spelled differently, then they are called heterographs. Find heterographs meaning:

CONDIMENT and GATHERED

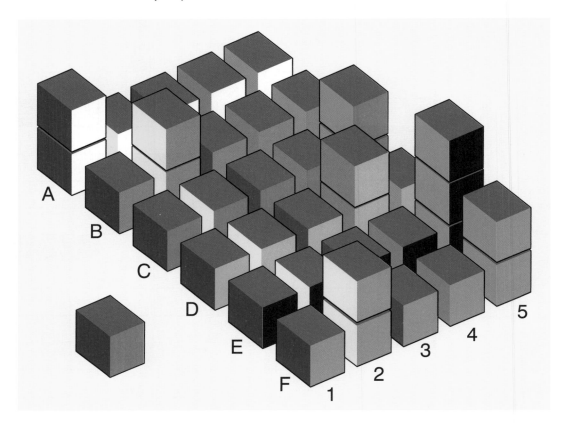

WORD SEARCH Material

All the words are hidden vertically, horizontally, or diagonally—in both directions. The letters that remain unused form a sentence from left to right.

```
T H E O L D C D R E L L I F E
L I O F S I T A R M A T E R I
A L S T T P H E E A T W E M R
T E U S S O E R B D G W E E G
D I A R E L N H B A R T U T A
A L N R A I L T U C A N V A S
E E I D M S E W R A N T E L C
R R I E E H T E M G U A L O A
H S E B D R A R A E L L I X N
T K S U O G N C O L A A E I I
I T O T R R I S F B T E Z D S
S E L O T S M T R R E U N E T
O S U N C I A K S A A N D A E
L T L A E N L I A M E N I M R
A O L N L T T A R P A U L I N
T N E A E E L O H R E S I N I
O E C D E R P A P E R C L A Y
R S E C N E F C I R T C E L E
```

- CANVAS
- CELLULOSE
- DIE
- ELASTIC
- ELECTRIC FENCE
- ELECTRODE
- EMAIL
- FILLER
- FOAM RUBBER
- FOIL
- GAS CANISTER
- GLAZE
- GRANULATE
- GROUT
- ISOLATOR
- LAMINATE
- MARBLE
- METAL OXIDE
- NANOTUBE
- PAPERCLAY
- POLISH
- RESIN
- ROPE
- SCREW THREAD
- SINTER
- STONE
- TARPAULIN
- THREAD
- TINDER

ACROSS

1 Purim month
5 Basic chord
10 Classic British sports cars
14 Get one's goat
15 Scope
16 Continental capital
17 Robin Hood's love
19 Nothing, to Pierre
20 Write on a tray
21 Gene in *Laura*
23 Need to indicate
24 Howard in *Gone With the Wind*
25 Chili con ___
27 Brunch hour
30 52 cards
33 Cauterize
35 Sports venue
36 "Why Not Take ___ of Me?"
37 Grassy fields
39 Pacific ___
40 Feudal sovereign
42 Industrial giant
43 Ancient Persian
44 Shoulder wear
46 Poetic name for Ireland
48 Detroit cager
50 Teeter-___
54 No-pay play
56 Pull off
57 Damon in *True Grit*
58 John Rolfe's love
60 Apropos of, in contracts
61 Acclimate
62 White-tailed eagle
63 Posterior
64 Spoiled (with "on")
65 90° on the compass

DOWN

1 Pistol-packing
2 Sam's love on *Cheers*
3 Do a wheel job
4 Las Vegas casino
5 Travel across
6 Like the Florida panther
7 Pasta suffix
8 Marble
9 Richards in *Blonde and Blonder*
10 "The more the ___"
11 Lancelot's love
12 Marcia Cross role
13 PlayStation 3 maker
18 Miss Bond in *Casino Royale*
22 Greek name for Greece
24 Ushers forth
26 Sans mixer
28 Geraint's love
29 Appellation
30 Mutt and Jeff, e.g.
31 Got down
32 Marc Antony's love
34 Surf sound
37 *With Reagan* memoirist
38 Miserable
41 Sparkle like gold
43 Afternoon show
45 "Keep it simple, ___!"
47 Greenwich Village neighbor
49 College town near Bangor
51 Aquarium fish
52 Chris in *Captain America*
53 Put back to 0
54 *The Kite Runner* narrator
55 Mare hair
56 Rhone feeder
59 Director's word

The Impossible Room

How observant are you? Take a look at the room below. Look a bit closer; Things are not quite as they seem. In fact, we've found more than 20 things wrong with this room. How many can you spot?

trivia

• Who starred with Kevin Costner in *The Bodyguard*?

Going Bing's Way

Harry Lillis "Bing" Crosby Jr. was already a star on radio and in the movies in 1944, when *Going My Way* debuted. His portrayal of a kindly priest who breathes new life into a failing parish was a fan and critical favorite and won him a best actor Oscar.

WHAT ELSE DO YOU KNOW OF THE VERSATILE DER BINGLE?

1 Where and in what year was Bing Crosby born?

_____

2 He sang it for the first time on his Kraft Music Hall radio show. Most experts agree that it's the No. 1 single of all time.

_____

3 This 1942 Bing movie inspired the name of a hotel chain.

_____

4 Bing's 1944 recording of it topped the charts for a week, but Billie Holiday's from the same year may be the better-known version of this sentimental song.

_____

5 These famous siblings joined Bing to record "Don't Fence Me In," which hit No. 1 in late '44.

_____

6 This song from *Going My Way* won an Oscar.

_____

7 In what 1945 movie did Bing reprise his beloved Father Chuck O'Malley role?

_____

8 What were the titles of the seven "Road" pictures he made with Bob Hope?

_____

_____

_____

_____

_____

_____

Sudoku Twin

Fill in the grid so that each row, each column, and each 3 x 3 frame contains every number from 1 to 9. A sudoku twin is two connected 9 x 9 sudokus.

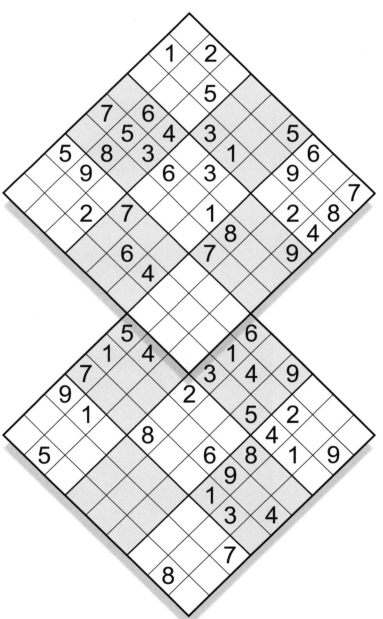

delete ONE

Delete one letter from

SMART CURING UTENSILS

and rearrange the rest to find a doctor's tool.

_____

_____

Spot the Differences

Find the nine differences in the image on the bottom right.

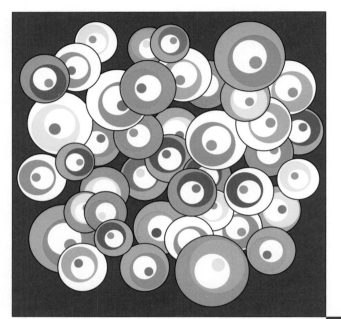

do you KNOW

Where did dodos live before they became extinct?

trivia

• Who sang "New York, New York" in the 1977 film?

CROSSWORD · Loves 2

ACROSS

1 "Amber Waves" singer Tori
5 Juggling ten balls, e.g.
9 Like some cats
14 Quilt stuffing
15 Span fraction
16 Quarter-round molding
17 Love of Ares
19 Speedster
20 Scrubbed
21 Got to
23 Piece of corn
24 ___ fever (tropical ailment)
25 Laundry problem
27 Teeterboard
30 "I Got You ___": Sonny & Cher
33 27th President
35 Fix Junior's shoelaces
36 Pub stock
37 Rot-resistant wood
39 Slip up
40 *Invisible Man* author Ellison
42 McGwire's 1998 rival
43 Gross seen on *Wildfire*
44 Insert more film
46 Some are ear-piercing
48 Check
50 Mortarboard topper
54 ___ replay
56 Not ersatz
57 Marry again
58 Love of Perseus
60 Empty-headed
61 Low in fat
62 Seth's son
63 Puts on cloud nine
64 Danny in *The Court Jester*
65 Cupid's missile

DOWN

1 Rearward
2 Leaf on the Canadian flag
3 "On the ___ hand ..."
4 Peculiar
5 Accuracy
6 *Idylls of the King* lady
7 Make it happen
8 "___ Goes My Baby": Drifters
9 Food seekers
10 One in a Red Cross shelter
11 Jane Eyre's love
12 Not windward
13 "My Sweet ___": Harrison
18 Real standout
22 Half-picas
24 Freezer cycle
26 Atlas pages
28 Ethereal
29 *The Way We ___* (1973)
30 Comedienne Roseanne
31 Side petals
32 Edward Cullen's love
34 Final, say
37 Party game
38 Wine from noble rot
41 Forebode
43 Took for granted
45 Relaxation room
47 Paul in *Little Miss Sunshine*
49 Follow stealthily
51 City near Assisi
52 *Return of the Jedi* moon
53 "Last, but not ___"
54 Garden perennial
55 Oahu goose
56 Aussie greeting
59 Teachers' org.

Energy Saver

Brian drew up a diagram to drastically reduce the amount of oil his transport company uses. How many barrels does he aim to use?

19247   7429 924 42   ?

DOUBLETALK

Homophones are words that share the same pronunciation, no matter how they are spelled. If they are spelled differently, then they are called heterographs. Find heterographs meaning:

DARING and PERFORMED A PASTIME

_____

WORD POWER Vocabulary-building

Does your lexicon need a lift?
Try these terms guaranteed to impress even the most well-versed wordsmiths,
from the vocabulary-building book *Talk Like a Genius* by Ed Kozak. Stumped?

. . . .

1. **capitulate** (kuh-'pih-chuh-layt) *v.*—A: provide funding. B: stop resisting. C: state formally.

2. **unequivocal** (uhn-ih-'kwih-vuh-kuhl) *adj.*—A: cool under pressure. B: untamed or out of control. C: leaving no doubt.

3. **cavalier** (ka-vuh-'lir) *adj.*—A: nonchalant or marked by disdainful dismissal. B: dome-shaped. C: undefeated or worthy of praise.

4. **leery** ('lir-ee) *adj.*—A: untrusting. B: odd. C: off balance.

5. **levity** ('leh-vuh-tee) *n.*—A: taxation. B: merriment. C: departure.

6. **penchant** ('pen-chunt) *n.*—A: recital. B: strong liking. C: deep thought.

7. **bifurcate** ('biy-fer-kayt) *v.*—A: tell lies. B: flash like lightning. C: divide into parts.

8. **craven** ('kray-vuhn) *adj.*—A: chiseled. B: needy or famished. C: cowardly.

9. **coterie** ('koh-tuh-ree) *n.*—A: exclusive group. B: takeover. C: birdcage.

10. **stalwart** ('stahl-wert) *adj.*—A: loyal. B: left-handed. C: disguising one's weakness.

11. **travesty** ('tra-vuh-stee) *n.*—A: wardrobe. B: long journey on foot. C: absurd imitation.

12. **hedonism** ('hee-duh-nih-zuhm) *n.*—A: espionage. B: sun worship. C: pursuit of pleasure.

13. **obviate** ('ahb-vee-ayt) *v.*—A: watch over. B: prevent or render unnecessary. C: leave unfinished.

14. **excoriate** (ek-'skor-ee-ayt) *v.*—A: hollow out. B: criticize harshly. C: sketch in detail.

15. **penurious** (peh-'nur-ee-uhs) *adj.*—A: given to fits of rage. B: wordy. C: poor.

Inside Man

ACROSS

1 Prefix for bucks
5 Malia Obama's sister
10 Radar sweep
14 Lollapalooza
15 Actor's study
16 Green cup
17 Firebug
19 Post-Passover period
20 He anointed Saul
21 ___ Innocent (1990)
23 Corner sign
25 West Side Story girl
26 Rio's "Christ the ___"
30 Threefold
33 Folk rocker DiFranco
34 Passover meal
36 Provide (with)
37 Smooch
39 Claire in Homeland
41 Fellow
42 Hiding a derringer
44 Slowly, in music
46 Old verb ending
47 Bag holder, of sorts
49 2011 Spielberg film
51 Nose openings
53 Vault
54 Door, e.g.
57 Melodic
61 FDR's Scottie
62 Mudpuppy
64 Deduction for waste
65 Exhilarate
66 Cork locale
67 "Smooth Operator" singer
68 Frighten off
69 Start a poker game

DOWN

1 Swiffers
2 "Orinoco Flow" singer
3 Microbe
4 Work up
5 Competed in Super G
6 Got an ___ (aced)
7 Make paper dolls
8 "I ___ Symphony": Supremes
9 Upward slope
10 Crying out loud?
11 Hijack
12 Nautical adverb
13 Disappointing date
18 Passes out
22 Milord
24 Floorboard item
26 Moroccan hub
27 Make used (to)
28 Took apart
29 Stay on for another year
31 Some wedding guests
32 River of forgetfulness
35 Kidney-related
38 Disjoined
40 Ticker tape at a parade, e.g.
43 Kid-vid explorer
45 Maureen in McLintock!
48 Grew rigid
50 Theorized
52 Richter ___
54 Pond youngsters
55 Old capital of Japan
56 Israeli resort city
58 Cartoon canine
59 Roman evening
60 Pitcher Hershiser
63 Chowed down

WORD SEARCH **Scrappy Scarecrow**

All the words associated with a familiar fall figure are hidden vertically, horizontally, or diagonally—in both directions.

```
Q  P  D  H  T  C  E  T  O  R  P  C  V  V  Y  T  R  S  M
R  W  S  G  U  A  R  D  Y  R  T  N  E  S  R  D  O  J  F
O  F  J  S  T  Q  T  O  Z  D  Q  D  S  S  J  Y  C  W  Y
I  S  O  J  T  D  E  C  O  Y  I  W  F  E  M  X  O  N  R
W  J  H  A  L  L  O  W  E  E  N  B  C  L  N  J  S  P  T
Z  Z  V  G  O  A  J  K  C  U  R  W  J  E  Z  N  T  A  N
H  S  S  X  J  J  U  P  D  A  O  N  T  C  R  M  U  C  U
V  I  P  T  F  U  O  Q  I  R  I  H  G  G  N  X  M  D  O
O  D  O  L  P  S  J  N  K  U  G  G  N  Q  D  F  E  E  C
V  F  R  E  T  X  L  B  Q  I  B  I  D  E  V  A  A  E  B
E  B  C  M  L  E  O  E  R  U  F  U  C  I  A  M  A  S  I
R  F  O  U  S  O  N  F  Y  F  H  O  R  Y  N  O  W  P  T
A  B  J  S  T  N  E  E  U  D  R  O  Q  L  N  C  G  N  P
L  J  B  S  A  O  I  T  D  A  R  C  V  H  A  S  L  B  N
L  P  J  M  G  E  S  G  T  R  U  Z  T  K  D  P  O  I  U
S  W  Z  Z  V  H  X  I  F  W  A  S  X  K  N  E  V  R  B
M  H  K  M  I  D  O  L  T  D  E  G  Y  X  A  T  E  D  E
Q  O  C  O  R  N  F  I  E  L  D  S  Q  W  B  B  S  S  O
S  B  K  S  M  P  L  Z  Z  W  A  R  T  S  E  T  Y  A  R
```

- BANDANNA
- BIRDS
- BRAINLESS
- BURLAP
- CORNFIELD
- COSTUME
- COUNTRY
- CROPS
- DECORATION
- DECOY
- FRIGHTEN
- GARDEN
- GLOVES
- GUARD
- HALLOWEEN
- MANNEQUIN
- OVERALLS
- POST
- PROTECT
- SEED CAP
- SENTRY
- STRAW
- STUFFING
- WORK BOOTS

Sport Maze

Draw the shortest way from the ball to the goal. You can only move along vertical and horizontal lines, not along diagonal lines. The figure on each square indicates the number of squares the ball must be moved in the same direction. You can change direction at each stop.

3	3	3	3	1	2
2	1	4	3	1	⬤
3	4	3	1	3	4
5	2	2	1	4	5
5	2	1	1	2	4
1	2	3	5	2	3

do you KNOW?

What did
Dr. James Naismith
invent?

ONE LETTER LESS OR MORE

The word on the right side contains the letters of the word on the left side, plus or minus the letter in the middle. One letter is already in the right place.

N A V I G A T E -A   [ ] I [ ] [ ] [ ] [ ]

CROSSWORD Outside Man

ACROSS

1 Follower of Mary
5 Sits in judgment
10 FBI agents
14 "Dies ___" (Latin hymn)
15 Throw with great effort
16 Recherché
17 Naval Academy student
19 Kitchen addition?
20 *Batman Begins* actor Liam
21 Like *Up*
23 Printer's buys
25 Shade of gray
26 Jester
30 Come into one's own
33 Troy, NY school
34 Black cattle breed
36 Deathly pale
37 Coastal eagles
39 Clark in *The Misfits*
41 Muscle fitness
42 He visits once a year
44 Ford Field team
46 Surround
47 Gas-bill units
49 Suspect's request
51 Pleases
53 Like a Bose system
54 Lengthen
57 White water
61 *Hud* director
62 Overall strategy
64 Zoological wings
65 Hair braid
66 Feudal fieldhand
67 Patch up
68 Aerosol, e.g.
69 Fake out the goalie

DOWN

1 Describe in detail
2 "Voyage to India" Grammy winner
3 Fabricated
4 Jazz legend Smith
5 Cerebral activity
6 Salesman
7 "___ Rock": Simon & Garfunkel
8 Chris in *Captain America*
9 Demential
10 Superlative for Ali
11 Swiss peak
12 *Athena* artist
13 Indispensability
18 Accord, for one
22 Spice Girls hit
24 Katey of *8 Simple Rules* ...
26 Blazer patch
27 Winfrey in *Native Son*
28 Lake Wobegone resident
29 Woolen head scarf
31 Robin Williams voiced a blue one
32 The opposition
35 Laziness
38 Acted like a peacock
40 Sum total
43 "Abdul Abulbul ___" (nonsense song)
45 Up to the present
48 They're stuck in corners
50 Buff
52 Sell, in a greedy way
54 Hyde Park buggy
55 Churn up
56 Captain of industry
58 Dutch singer DeLange
59 Clammy
60 Old-fashioned dagger
63 Mexican relative

In the Know with Nutrition

Do you understand what's what with all those fats, carbs, sugars, and more in your food?
This healthy checklist of questions may help you pinpoint any weak spots.

1. In terms of protein content, how do beans differ from fish, meat, and eggs?

   _____

2. A diet rich in saturated fats raises the levels of what in your blood?

   _____

3. What are the common names of lactose and fructose?

   _____

4. Does a gram of fat give you more, less, or about the same energy as a gram of carbohydrate?

   _____

5. What vital fluid has no nutritional value whatsoever?

   _____

6. What's a good source of monounsaturated fat: smoked salmon or olive oil?

   _____

7. What is the name of the scientific study of food and diet?

   _____

8. What are the chemical components of protein?

   _____

9. What substance found in wheat and rye must be avoided by people with celiac disease?

   _____

10. What is the only macronutrient whose lack can lead to a deficiency disease?

    _____

11. Energy is transferred from the food we eat to our bodies through what?

    _____

12. How much fiber should a person digest every day?

    _____

13. What food is the largest single source of saturated fat in the American diet?

    _____

14. What water-soluble vitamin is stored in the body?

    _____

Word Sudoku

Complete the grid so that each row, each column, and each 3 x 3 frame contains the nine letters from the black box below. The hidden nine-letter word is in the diagonal from top left to bottom right.

A G H L N R S T Y

	N	T		R				
Y	A		G		S			
			A				G	
A	R		L			N		
		S					Y	H
T	H			G	N	R		
			R			T	N	
		N	H			S	R	
	G	R				H		

do you KNOW?

In which novel is
Lucy Snow
the heroine?

UNCANNY TURN

Rearrange the letters of the phrase below to form a cognate anagram, one that is related or connected in meaning to the original phrase. The answer can be one or more words.

AFFLICT RIGHTS

Sewing Basket

ACROSS

1 Tasty crustaceans
6 Measuring abbreviation in recipes
9 Abbreviation for Lorne Michaels' TV show airing since 1975
12 All the vowels
13 Eureka!
14 Mauna ___ Volcano
15 Branches
16 A pin ___ is found in a sewing basket
18 Twirled in a parade
20 ___ of Green Gables
21 Zodiac sign of the twins
24 Little ones
25 Prayer ending
26 Measuring ___ is found in a sewing basket
29 Measure of luminosity
30 Edgar ___ Poe
31 Barnyard sound
34 A ___ ripper is found in a sewing basket
35 Geek
36 Desolate
40 Took the skin off an apple
42 Othello's enemy
43 Humiliation
45 Finger protector found in a sewing basket
47 Found the sum total
51 Charged atom
52 Piece of Mr. Potato Head
53 ___ Lucy (TV show, 2 words)
54 Not positive (abbreviation)
55 A pair
56 Allowable

DOWN

1 The Golden State (abbrev.)
2 Sporting goods store
3 Direct to a target
4 Certain thread holder found in a sewing basket
5 ___ B. Anthony
6 Mexican staple
7 Have nothing to do with
8 Faux ___
9 Move in a stealthy way
10 Not a soul (2 words)
11 Areas in a bowling alley
17 Horse food
19 Found on a book cover
21 Lady
22 Large flightless bird
23 Tex-___ cuisine
24 Highest score, often
27 Pie ___ mode (2 words)
28 Texas panhandle city
30 Request
31 Controversial actor Gibson
32 Earthy mineral
33 Strange
35 Item with an eye found in a sewing basket
36 Peaceful protest of the '60s (hyphenated)
37 Nevada lake
38 Growing older
39 CD-___
41 Internet message
43 Shredded cabbage dish
44 Superman, for one
46 Wager
48 Pooch
49 Actress Longoria
50 Dover's state (abbreviation)

WORD SEARCH ▸ **Cabin Fever**

All the words representing surefire cures that will cool down your cabin fever are hidden vertically, horizontally, or diagonally—in both directions.

E	U	W	I	M	M	Y	M	O	H	N	J	P	X	G	P	J	E	P
Q	S	Z	O	H	H	S	L	S	O	H	P	Z	Z	N	N	H	X	X
G	A	I	T	V	L	Z	B	R	Y	S	K	M	M	I	C	X	H	O
X	N	O	U	Y	J	A	C	G	K	Z	B	Z	U	I	C	M	T	B
K	A	A	R	R	W	P	C	A	H	I	M	E	S	K	M	K	J	E
Z	G	I	V	I	C	Y	T	B	R	D	I	G	E	S	F	E	O	X
S	G	E	S	S	M	I	E	D	S	S	M	J	U	S	K	T	K	E
O	O	B	V	E	N	R	W	Z	U	C	O	F	M	W	Y	A	E	R
I	B	T	V	G	M	A	P	N	G	N	I	D	A	E	R	R	W	C
X	O	V	R	O	T	A	S	K	C	F	C	L	Q	B	Y	O	A	I
P	T	V	M	C	B	H	G	L	E	R	E	C	T	A	A	C	I	S
Z	G	I	H	O	I	E	E	F	N	B	S	Z	L	K	X	E	H	E
Q	T	R	N	N	V	A	L	F	T	T	A	R	C	E	O	D	O	Y
P	L	Q	E	O	N	I	O	K	E	B	C	Y	O	M	Z	E	B	P
B	K	V	G	K	M	X	E	C	R	A	F	T	S	O	U	R	B	K
F	L	A	N	R	U	O	J	M	T	K	P	A	N	M	D	S	Y	Y
J	B	T	K	K	D	R	K	L	A	W	Q	R	J	U	A	T	I	V
A	H	M	T	M	X	F	E	L	I	B	O	M	W	O	N	S	U	C
J	D	Z	E	X	K	A	D	I	N	Z	S	D	R	A	C	B	I	O

- BAKE
- BIRD-WATCH
- CARDS
- CLEAN
- CRAFTS
- CRUISE
- ENTERTAIN
- EXERCISE
- GAMES
- HOBBY
- JOURNAL
- MOVIE
- MUSEUM
- MUSIC
- NAP
- OUTDOORS
- READING
- REDECORATE
- SKATING
- SKIING
- SNOWMOBILE
- SUNSHINE
- TOBOGGAN
- WALK

Number Cluster

Cubes showing numbers have been placed on the grid below, with some spaces left empty. Can you complete the grid by creating runs of the same number and of the same length as the number? So, where a cube with number 5 has been included on the grid, you need to create a run of five number 5's, including the cube already shown. The run can be horizontal, vertical, or both horizontal and vertical.

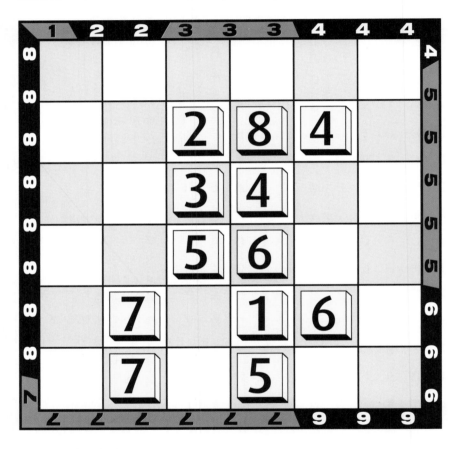

SANDWICH

What five-letter word belongs between the word at left and the word at right, so that the first and second word, and the second and third word, each form a common compound word or phrase?

S E A _ _ _ _ _ M A R K

CROSSWORD **Blues Singers**

ACROSS
1 Freeway exit
5 Great deal
10 Novel essence
14 Aka Lamb
15 Utter devastation
16 Himalayan hulk
17 "Blue Monday" singer
19 Assign an NC-17, say
20 Shilly-shallies
21 Powell in *Born to Dance*
23 Larter in *Final Destination*
24 ___ *Yankees!* (1958)
25 What a weary motorist may look for
29 Leaves the rat race
32 "Dies ___" (Latin hymn)
33 Yawned
35 Tiddlywink, e.g.
36 Tyler in *Jersey Girl*
37 Vallone in *Nevada Smith*
38 NYC subway org.
39 Hawaiian neckwear
41 Partner of dangerous
43 Touch
44 Along in years
46 Newly edited
48 Novelist Ellis
49 Ballpoint
50 Plug in a tub
53 Gels
57 Rob of *Parks and Recreation*
58 "Blue Bayou" singer
60 Burnett of CNN
61 Chris of tennis
62 Former Japanese capital
63 Battle the bulge
64 College VIPs
65 *Forrest* ___ (1994)

DOWN
1 Striped whistle-blowers
2 Maple seeds
3 Tiny parasite
4 Biblical verse
5 Exhibition
6 Rotating machine pieces
7 Marvel Studios founder Arad
8 Cooked well
9 Rebuked
10 Cheops construction
11 "Blue" singer
12 Camp Swampy dog
13 Stadium level
18 "The Persistence of Memory" painter
22 Scarf down
25 City in N France
26 Fancy window
27 "Blue Jean" singer
28 Cartoonist Trudeau
29 Attribute
30 First name in cosmetics
31 Burn milk
34 Non-stick spray
40 Caduceus figure
41 Modified
42 Leaves
43 Discovery
45 Spokesperson
47 Win or lose, e.g.
50 Snowmobile
51 "Time" singer Amos
52 Wander
53 Telephone, slangily
54 Genesis twin
55 Average
56 Hypnotic trance breaker
59 Pro vote

Furniture

All the words are hidden vertically, horizontally, or diagonally—in both directions. The letters that remain unused form a sentence from left to right.

```
T A P E S T R Y T A C H A P N
O D E L I E E R I E S A B M R
A T E P R A C S N C R H E A D
X D T B A R S T O O L O E L C
O T O O R A T I V L E C B E I
B E L I M E L D A R C N G A E
E U M N I A T R U C D O U N T
K Q A P A I N T I N G E T E I
U U D I H L I G H T F I S X U
J O T C R S D N I L B U R K S
D B N E W M I T O A H B K C E
T E W O O R A O M S B O N O G
B O B R E A T T R H U O A M N
M S B X E S A R T T F K B M U
C U P B O A R D I R F C A A O
W A T E R B E D N A E A F H L
D N A T S T A H G Y T S O L I
E M A R F R O O D G H E S T S
```

- AIR MATTRESS
- ASHTRAY
- BARSTOOL
- BENCH
- BLINDS
- BOOKCASE
- BOUQUET
- BOX BED
- BUFFET
- CARPET
- CLOSET
- CRADLE
- CUPBOARD
- CURTAIN
- DESK
- DOOR FRAME
- HAMMOCK
- HAT STAND
- JUKEBOX
- LAMP
- LOUNGE SUITE
- OTTOMAN
- PAINTING
- SOFA BANK
- STOOL
- TABORET
- TAPESTRY
- WATERBED

Keep Going

Start on a blank square of your choice and connect as many blank squares as possible with one single continuous line. You can only connect squares along vertical and horizontal lines, not along diagonal lines. You must continue the connecting lineup until the next obstacle, i.e., the border of the box, a black square, or a square that has already been used. You can change direction at any obstacle you meet. Each square can only be used once. The number of blank squares that will be left unused is marked in the upper square. There is more than one solution. We only show one solution.

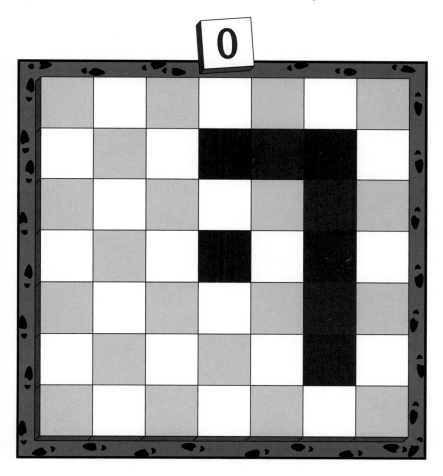

do you **KNOW**

Which country is Greenland part of?

Futoshiki

Fill in the 5 x 5 grid with the numbers from 1 to 5 once per row and column, while following the greater-than/lesser-than symbols shown. There is only one valid solution that can be reached through logic and clear thinking alone!

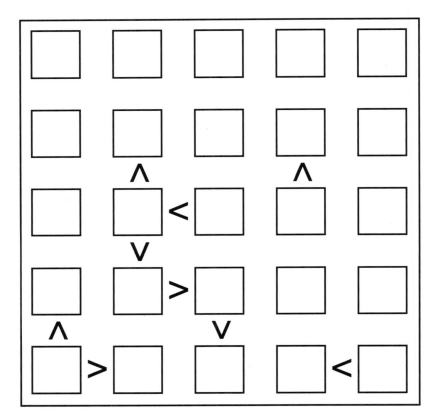

trivia
- Who was born Constance Ockelman?

LETTERBLOCKS

Move the letterblocks around so that words associated with the cards are formed on the top and bottom rows.

WEATHER CHART **Sunny**

Where will the sun shine? With the knowledge that each arrow points to a place where a symbol should be, can you locate the sunny spots? The symbols cannot be next to each other vertically, horizontally, or diagonally. A symbol cannot be placed on top of an arrow. We show one symbol.

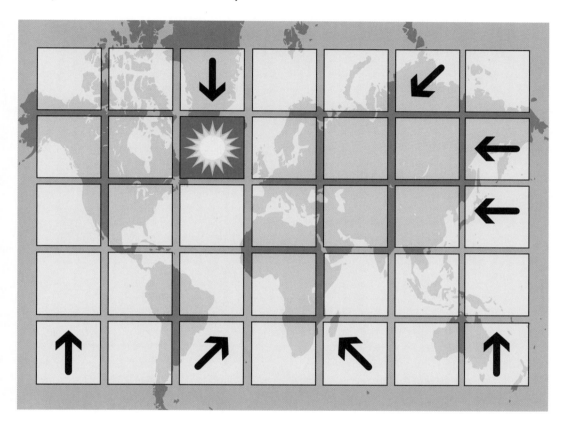

TRIANAGRAM

Three-word groups of anagrams are also called triplets or trianagrams.
Complete the group:

S L U M P _ _ _ _ _   _ _ _ _ _

More Than a Walk

ACROSS

1 Shuttle type
6 Elisabeth in *Hollow Man*
10 Fairway hazard
14 Wyoming range
15 Site of a ship's controls
16 Coney Island thrill
17 Clubs for Rickie Fowler
18 Florentine river
19 Ian Fleming's alma mater
20 Track rivalries?
23 It can be bruised or massaged
24 Ending with baron
25 Everlasting
29 Macy's department
33 Port revenue
34 Great lake
36 State of agitation
37 Perp identifier
38 Barbecue spices
39 Mineral suffix
40 "That's hot!"
42 Sagan and Sandburg
44 Former times
45 Stage background
47 *Pollyanna* author Porter
49 Prefix for graphic
50 Mandela's org.
51 Red Grange's nickname
59 "Get Back" singer Lovato
60 March flier
61 Rockefeller Center statue
62 Eve's grandson
63 *Lawrence of Arabia* is one
64 Davis in *Speechless*
65 Launder
66 Rolltop
67 Award honoring Poe

DOWN

1 Word with fried or crazy
2 Bolivia neighbor
3 Like ___ of bricks
4 Sean in *The Russia House*
5 Standard
6 Chase baseballs
7 Savory plant
8 Bone of the arm
9 "I Second That ___": Miracles
10 Garden frame
11 Initiation
12 Bustles of activity
13 Pigsty
21 Yannick of tennis
22 Do needlework
25 Arnold and Duchin
26 Tennis skirt
27 Tour de France stage
28 Caverns of Virginia
29 Majestic
30 Lyonnaise ingredient
31 Cardio med
32 Longhorn
35 Capek's robot play
41 Muffin type
42 Corrupt
43 Blast furnace residue
44 Raced a pleasure boat
46 Jellied fish
48 Mesh gears
51 Rowlands in *Hope Floats*
52 "Cornflake Girl" singer Tori
53 Popeye's tooter
54 Medical suffix
55 Margin of victory
56 Couturier Cassini
57 Capital of Yemen
58 Peter the Great, e.g.
59 Morning moisture

BRAINSNACK® Lucky Number

Which number should be crossed out in the last grid?

DOUBLETALK

Homophones are words that share the same pronunciation, no matter how they are spelled. If they are spelled differently, then they are called heterographs. Find heterographs meaning:

GROUND GRAIN and BLOOM

Sport Maze

Draw the shortest way from the ball to the goal. You can only move along vertical and horizontal lines, not along diagonal lines. The figure on each square indicates the number of squares the ball must be moved in the same direction. You can change direction at each stop.

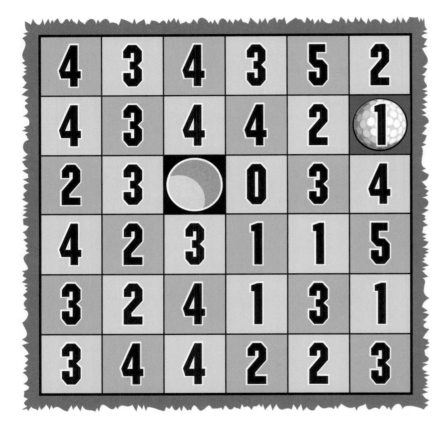

do you KNOW

Who founded the Paralympic Games?

_____

ONE LETTER LESS OR MORE

The word on the right side contains the letters of the word on the left side, plus or minus the letter in the middle. One letter is already in the right place.

P A R A D I S E +P ☐ ☐ ☐ ☐ P ☐ ☐ ☐ ☐

CROSSWORD # Football Season

ACROSS

1 Letters
6 Trend
9 A pouch in an animal
12 Ice crystals
13 Hotel
14 Not an amateur
15 Sri ___
16 Football arena
18 Furious
20 Country singer McEntire
21 Part of a football uniform
24 Plateaus
25 Margarine
26 Eight, prefix
29 Bacon source
30 Not silently
31 Supermarket chain
34 Dab at
35 Catch, as on a sweater
36 Fundamental
40 Bring an opponent down, in football
42 Scent
43 One at ___ (2 words)
45 Plays against the offense, in football
47 Bother
51 Greek terrorist group from the 1970s (abbreviation)
52 Atmosphere
53 Fathered
54 ___ Moines, Iowa
55 Sound used to indicate a collision
56 Permanent marks on skin

DOWN

1 Professional football organization (abbreviation)
2 Passage opening
3 Heavy weight
4 Inuit
5 Look at intently
6 Clenched hand
7 Feed the kitty
8 Genetic material
9 Secret agents
10 Antilles island
11 States of unconsciousness
17 Rapper Dr ___
19 Coral island circling a lagoon
21 Jump on one foot
22 Inventor Whitney
23 "He doesn't have a ___ to stand on"
24 1960s style
27 Talk like a baby or pigeon
28 ___ frutti
30 *Good Morning America* TV network
31 Pen need
32 Lady
33 "___ is just a number"
35 Picturesque
36 Portended
37 "Rolling in the Deep" singer
38 Couches
39 Intense anger
41 Collect
43 Nepal's continent
44 Semester
46 Catch
48 Gun owner's org.
49 "___ the ramparts we watched"
50 Football field measurements (abbreviation)

Against the Clock

The winner has run the distance in 15 seconds, the second in 21 seconds, etc. How many seconds will it take the sixth athlete to cross the line?

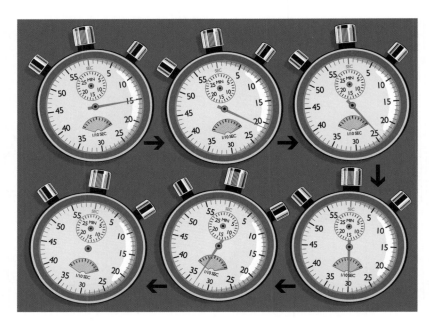

QUICK WORD SEARCH

Find the musical terms listed below in the word search grid.

```
K T E C N A N O S E R O C N E
E O O O O B B L I G A T O N E
Y N N O P R O G R E S S I O N
L A I T R A P O L Y P H O N Y
C L E F R O T C U D N O C M P
```

CANON CLEF CONDUCTOR ENCORE KEY OBBLIGATO ART PARTIAL POLYPHONY

TRIVIA QUIZ # Doctor, Doctor

Do you have the right answers to these slippery questions tucked away in your medicine bag?

1. What painkiller is related to the cricket bat?

_____

2. Who might use a nebulizer?

_____

3. What is the ancient Chinese practice of sticking fine needles into a person called?

_____

4. What poisonous garden plant is used to produce a powerful heart medicine?

_____

5. What invention of Wilhelm Roentgen revolutionized modern medicine by allowing doctors to see inside the human body?

_____

6. Alexander Fleming is credited with discovering which antibiotic after studying the growth of mold?

_____

7. In alternative medicine, what name is given to the practice of exposing the body to ultra-dilute solutions?

_____

8. Warfarin, once used as a rat poison, is used to treat what medical condition?

_____

9. For what surgical procedures is Dr. Magdi Yacoub famous?

_____

10. By what name is nitrous oxide more commonly known?

_____

11. How many bones does a normal adult have?

_____

12. What is the name of the last part of the small intestine?

_____

13. What condition causes the skin to turn yellow?

_____

14. What is the hardest part of the normal human body?

_____

The Billionaire Club

ACROSS

1 Move heavily
5 Calculator symbol
9 Group of secret schemers
14 German "A"
15 Galley workers
16 Rafa's friend
17 Encore Las Vegas developer
19 Serbian-born tennis star
20 They take things the wrong way
21 Bright red
23 One side of a trade
24 "You're making ___ mistake!"
25 Vending machine bills
27 New York boundary river
30 Lurid fiction
33 Place to recline
35 Suffix for psych
36 ___ carte
37 Produced
38 Baseball season in Montreal
39 Concerning, in legalese
41 Spanish hero played by Heston
43 Male monarch
44 Spin a yarn
46 Scion, for one
48 Jedi trainer
49 *The Wizard of Oz* setting
53 Pill
56 Alberta hockey city
57 Make use of
58 Dallas Mavericks owner
60 Leg of lamb
61 CCLXIII x IV
62 Thus, to a logician
63 Paradises
64 White linen robes
65 Wimbledon ranking

DOWN

1 Unwanted bugs
2 Gracefully flexible
3 Poker player Longson
4 Come to pass
5 Supplied fuel
6 Minstrel songs
7 Large coffeepot
8 Tax IDs
9 Muskmelon
10 Explorer Vespucci
11 Microsoft cofounder
12 *CIA Diary* author
13 Got the bronze
18 Like 10, 20, and 30
22 Genesis exile
26 Go laterally
27 Petrova of tennis
28 Lovely Beatles girl
29 Big name in PCs
30 Distress
31 Funny bone
32 Google cofounder
34 London's Old ___ Theatre
40 Canyon cause
41 Latin for "and others"
42 Loser to Bush in 1988
43 Languages
45 Minor guardians
47 Poolroom powder
50 Buffalo wing
51 ___ *in Harlem* (1991)
52 Ecclesiastical meeting
53 Tweety's home
54 Rah-rah
55 *Nanny McPhee* star Thompson
56 Nursery fixture
59 Part of APB

WORD SEARCH The Adventures of Tintin

All the words are hidden vertically, horizontally, or diagonally—in both directions. The letters that remain unused form a sentence from left to right.

```
A Y W O N S T H E S E C R N E
E R T P A R C H M E N T A N N
O F I T S C R O L L H E E E I
U T N S I C O R N I P K S B R
T A N R T F I L M O O C W A A
S D I E R I E C R R T O A R H
I E D T T B D U B S N P L N K
L Y S S T E E E E O E K L A A
A L V I E N P V S S P C E B S
N I T N I T I M I S E I T Y N
R A L I B T O N O E I P R G O
U R B S C H T A E C S L E S S
O T D E T H O N A L N C K A P
J O T M G I C M B O O I O I M
K E C I R E A O T E D T H L O
D B F Y T H E D B E L S S I H
G R E T S A M E E R H T I N T
A N A R T I S L T H E R G G E
```

- ARISTIDES SILK
- BARNABY
- BROKEN
- DETECTIVES
- EUROPEAN
- FIGHT
- INCOMPETENT
- JOURNALIST
- MODEL
- PARCHMENT
- PICKPOCKET
- SAILING
- SAKHARINE
- SCROLL
- SHIP
- SINISTER
- SNOWY
- STOLEN
- THOMPSON
- THOMSON
- THREE-MASTER
- TINTIN
- TRAIL
- WALLET

Sudoku

Fill in the grid so that each row, each column, and each 3 x 3 frame contains every number from 1 to 9.

				6	3	8		5
	6		7			9		
9		8	1				4	
4					7			1
	1		2	8	5	7		
5			4					8
1					9	3		6
	9				6	4		
8		6	3	7				

trivia

• Who did Gregory Peck portray in *To Kill a Mockingbird?*

SYMBOL SUMS

Can you work out these number sums using three of these four symbols? $+ - \div \times$

3 ☐ 3 ☐ 18 ☐ 9 = 9

CROSSWORD 4-Syllable Words 1

ACROSS

1 Dutch painter of "The Jolly Toper"
5 San Antonio landmark
10 *Star Trek II: The Wrath of ___* (1982)
14 Menu bar option
15 Old treasure
16 Speed contest
17 Not doable
19 Humorist Bombeck
20 Milk farms
21 Prison, slangily
23 An ocean
24 Architect's plinth
25 Emanate
27 Violin quartet?
30 Slaps on
33 Kentucky Derby entrants
35 Egyptian lifeline
36 Weeks in a Roman calendar
37 Early space station
38 Use scissors
39 Pear variety
41 Eye color
43 Aoudad dads
44 Gaming areas
46 Brazil soccer great
48 Olive genus
49 Safe from break-ins
53 Go around
56 Viewing screen
57 Concluded
58 Request from a host
60 Polo in *Meet the Parents*
61 *Despicable Me* girl
62 Sweet charity
63 Gross in *Coupe de Ville*
64 Star-crossed lover
65 In the event that

DOWN

1 Model Klum
2 Don Draper, for one
3 Fatty compound
4 Isherwood's *The Berlin ___*
5 Rat poison
6 Floral neckwear
7 Clerical robe
8 Wire measures
9 Spotted cats
10 Moscow landmark
11 Bob Dylan plays one
12 Cartoon supply company
13 Dear partner
18 Old Thailand
22 JFK posting: Abbr.
26 Berdych of tennis
27 Throat infection
28 Not at all cheerful
29 Court units
30 *Fantastic Four* star Jessica
31 Christian of fashion
32 Find
34 "Supernova" singer Phair
40 Dieter's measure
41 More weighty
42 Enclave of South Africa
43 Music student's solo
45 Marina ___ Rey
47 Headey of *Game of Thrones*
50 Beneficial
51 "Clue" choices
52 John ___ Steinbeck
53 Roster
54 By any chance
55 Conductor Akira
56 Tiny arachnid
59 Energy

Wheeling Around

The map below shows the route followed by a group of cyclists. What is the first letter of the city the cyclists will visit after Carcassonne?

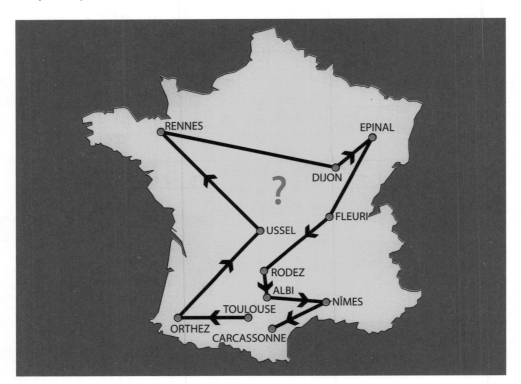

LETTER LINE

Put a letter in each of the squares below to make a word that is a meeting for contests. The number clues refer to other words that can be made from the whole.

4 8 7 5 6 9 10 LEFTOVER • 5 8 3 1 4 2 5 A PARTICLE WITHOUT CHARGE; 1 6 5 10 4 3 7 A DEMONSTRATION OF FRUSTRATION • 7 6 5 5 8 4 STYLE 10 2 4 7 8 9 1 AFFLICT WITH SUFFERING

1	2	3	4	5	6	7	8	9	10

WORD POWER — Language of Love

Before sending a card on Valentine's Day, be sure you know the language of love. Here are some words perfect for would-be Romeos and Juliets.

1. **ardent** ('ar-dent) *adj.*—
A: engaged. B: lyrical.
C: passionate.

2. **paramour** ('pa-ruh-mor) *n.*—
A: chaperone. B: lover. C: token
of affection.

3. **buss** ('buhs) *v.*—A: kiss. B: elope.
C: carve initials in a tree.

4. **swain** ('swayn) *n.*—A: intense
crush. B: male suitor. C: gondola
for two.

5. **connubial** (kuh-'new-bee-uhl)
adj.—A: coy. B: of marriage.
C: about the heart.

6. **troth** ('trawth) *n.*—A: wooden
or rustic altar. B: fidelity.
C: Celtic wedding ring.

7. **coquettish** (koh-'ket-ish) *adj.*—
A: flirtatious. B: alluring. C: shy.

8. **macushla** (muh-'koosh-luh)
n.—A: darling. B: fainting spell.
C: best man.

9. **platonic** (pluh-'tah-nik) *adj.*—
A: of a honeymoon. B: smitten.
C: without physical desire.

10. **liaison** (lee-'ay-zahn) *n.*—
A: secret affair. B: exchange of
vows. C: pet nickname.

11. **beaux** ('bohz) *n.*—
A: traditional string used
to join hands in marriage.
B: winks of an eye.
C: boyfriends.

12. **requite** (rih-'kwiyt) *v.*—
A: ask for someone's hand.
B: give back, as affection.
C: fondly remember.

13. **epistolary** (ih-'pis-tuh-la-ree)
adj.—A: serenading. B: set in an
arbor. C: relating to letters.

14. **philter** ('fil-ter) *n.*—A: love
potion. B: caress. C: family
keepsake or hand-me-down.

15. **cupidity** (kyu-'pih-duh-tee)
n.—A: valentine shape.
B: lust or desire for wealth.
C: condition of instant romance,
as love at first sight.

ACROSS

1 Moan and groan
5 Broken
10 Moola
14 Swan genus
15 Central New York city
16 Eight: Comb. form
17 Clambake fruit
19 College sports org.
20 Easily bent
21 Lends an ear
23 Lung in *Kung Fu Panda*
24 List abbr.
25 John of *Frasier*
29 Control pill
32 Revival cry
33 Puts aside
35 St. Andrews pothole
36 Prefix for function
37 Itsy
38 Brunched
39 "Beauty ___ the eye ..."
41 Angling leader
43 Florida-to-Calif. route
44 Ones providing arms?
46 Blue state
48 Platte River Indians
49 Subtle auction bid
50 Full of knowledge
53 Most unfair
57 *Ghostbusters* car
58 Slide rule's successor
60 In that case
61 Composer Montemezzi
62 ___ contendere
63 Towel marking
64 *The Merry Widow* composer
65 Murray of tennis

DOWN

1 Monk's cloak
2 Jai ___
3 Withers on the vine
4 *The Music Man* star
5 What bikinis expose
6 To ___ (with precision)
7 Wire diameter measure
8 Earth Day subj.
9 Jack ___ whiskey
10 Get in touch with
11 Quicken
12 *South Park* kid
13 2011 FedEx Cup winner
18 Field spaniel color
22 Depot: Abbr.
25 O'Rorke of song
26 Stockpile
27 Budgie of children's books
28 Shows boredom
29 Preps a banana
30 *Psycho* motel owner
31 Unlocks
34 Flashed sign
40 Department store section
41 Letter-writing device
42 Lethargy
43 Hoosier State
45 Shad delicacy
47 Midway prize
50 Green in *The Italian Job*
51 Dull pain
52 *The Help* director Taylor
53 *Daily Bruin* publisher
54 Hugh Laurie's alma mater
55 Realtor's sign
56 2004 Brad Pitt film
59 "Well, ___-di-dah"

Concentration—One Liner

Try to draw this shape with one continuous line without lifting your pencil off the page and without any overlapping.

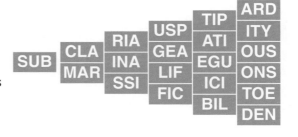

WORD WALL

Beginning at the left side of the wall, make a word by adding one group of letters from each column as you move left to right. When you have found the first word, go back to the second column and start the next word, gathering one group of letters from each column and so on until all the letters are used to make six words.

SUB	CLA	RIA	USP	TIP	ARD
	MAR	INA	GEA	ATI	ITY
		SSI	LIF	EGU	OUS
			FIC	ICI	ONS
				BIL	TOE
					DEN

Sunny

Where will the sun shine? With the knowledge that each arrow points to a place where a symbol should be, can you locate the sunny spots? The symbols cannot be next to each other vertically, horizontally, or diagonally. A symbol cannot be placed on top of an arrow. We show one symbol.

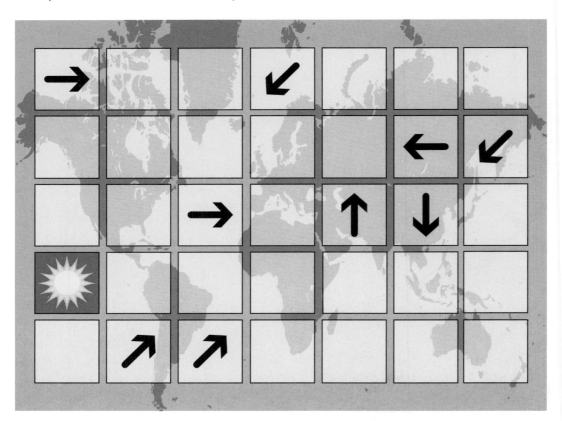

TRIANAGRAM

Three-word groups of anagrams are also called triplets or trianagrams.
Complete the group:

P S A L M _ _ _ _ _   _ _ _ _ _

CROSSWORD 4-Syllable Words 3

ACROSS
1 On ____ (not contracted)
5 Nurture
9 *Perry Mason* cop
14 Ark architect
15 *Legally Blonde* heroine
16 Alabama city
17 Like a new moon
19 *The Wizard of Oz* star
20 *I Was a ____ Werewolf* (1957)
21 Sun-dried grape
23 A, in Aachen
24 Throat problem
25 Winter Olympics event
29 Afternoon snooze
31 New York stage award
32 Discourage
34 Guess from left field
36 Female swan
37 Costa del ____
38 Shelley poem
39 Lumber along
41 Machine handle
43 *Garfield* diner owner
44 Fridge, old-style
46 Corbin of *Psych*
48 Mysterious saucers
49 ____ *for Vengeance*: Grafton
50 Gumshoe
52 One with gold crowns
56 Shoptalk
57 Crisis
59 Quagmire
60 Portrayal
61 Right away!
62 Longshot win
63 Intrepid
64 Make a fuss over

DOWN
1 Pique
2 Corn cake
3 Place for an icicle
4 Takeout cuisine
5 Affected
6 Hamburg's river
7 House add-on
8 A few bucks
9 Giveaway garb
10 Exercises logic
11 Swamp critters
12 FBI agents
13 *A Writer's Life* author Talese
18 Spinnaker or spanker, e.g.
22 Quite a distance
25 Comet Hale-____
26 ÷ symbols
27 Opera glasses, e.g.
28 Spay
29 Luminary
30 Luke Skywalker's mother
33 "Mazel ____!"
35 Kind of soup
40 Cabinet department
41 Forfeited
42 Idolized
43 "I'll Cry ____": Beatles
45 Purchased
47 Bout site
50 Kind of hockey shot
51 Sweet cicely, e.g.
52 Apple rival
53 ____ many words
54 Ella Fitzgerald genre
55 Use a keyboard
56 Dallas campus
58 Bovine sound

Hourglass

Starting in the middle, each word in the top half has the letters of the word below it, plus a new letter, and each word in the bottom half has the letters of the word above it, plus a new letter.

(1) Cuddling
(2) Gliding over a mountain slope
(3) Male monarchs
(4) Submerge
(5) Twirl
(6) European country
(7) Keyboards
(8) Strong emotion

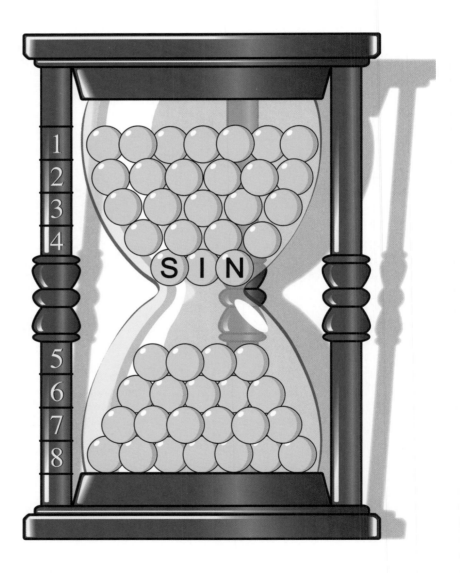

WORD SEARCH **Relationships**

All the words are hidden vertically, horizontally, or diagonally—in both directions. The letters that remain unused form a sentence from left to right.

```
H I R I B R I D E S M A I D N
E T A B I L E C G G R O O M A
E C R O V I D W E D D I N G P
C L A U W I D O W H O O D N N
E E R N O I T A R T S I G E R
R T I S A C T E N R E T N I S
E G A S R O C P G N H E N E L
M W O D M S E O G A N O I N A
O E L G N I S A N T I D H A T
N D T B O R G E R T D R P I I
Y D G I A E N A N U R O R T R
E I D E M C B I B I L A N A A
A N T E I O H I M Y P E C R M
I G N V U C A E G L B P U T A
T T I Q I S N A L A O O A W R
A L U L S O M P O O M V P H T
U E L A R Y I N E U R Y E R X
T O P E C E R T I F I C A T E
```

- BACHELOR
- BIGAMY
- BOUQUET
- BRIDESMAID
- BUDDIES
- CELIBATE
- CEREMONY
- CERTIFICATE
- CIVIL
- CONTRACT
- CORSAGE
- COURT
- DATE
- DIVORCE
- ENGAGEMENT
- EXTRAMARITAL
- GROOM
- HAPPINESS
- INTERNET
- LOVE
- MARRIAGE
- POLYGAMY
- REGISTRATION
- SINGLE
- TEARS
- WEDDING
- WIDOWHOOD

Winter Solstice

ACROSS

1 Period of time after winter solstice
5 Concede
8 Soda
12 Joanie Cunningham actress Moran
13 The night before
14 United ___ Emirates
15 Harry Potter tool
16 Winter solstice brings long hours of ___
18 Hibernation activity
20 Star Wars princess
21 Feel sick
23 "Hello" singer
27 Winter solstice brings the ___ day of the year
32 Water in Mexico
33 Like 32 Across
34 Star Trek actor George
36 Question's counterpart (abbr.)
37 Like a desert
39 Solstice marks the ___ of winter (2 words)
41 Afflict
43 Louisville to Chicago direction (abbr.)
44 Appearance
47 Grows weary
51 Winter solstice month
55 Mope
56 E in QED
57 Single
58 Clock's offering
59 Ocean motion
60 List abbreviation
61 Possible solstice forecast

DOWN

1 Some evergreens
2 Russia's ___ Mountains
3 Equator, for example
4 Ingratiate
5 Place for 18-Across
6 Rink shape
7 Existed
8 Its capital is Ottawa
9 Valuable rock
10 ___ Vegas
11 Stomach muscles
17 Sedona maker
19 Jolie's ex
22 Page
24 "Good heavens!"
25 ___ moth
26 Simple
27 Mop
28 This place
29 Last name in elevators
30 Take to the slopes
31 Seabird
35 Stevie Wonder's "___ She Lovely"
38 Erase
40 Winds around
42 ___ and Jerry
45 Woodwind
46 English county of Canterbury and Dover
48 Destroy
49 Furry red monster
50 Distort
51 Droplets on grass
52 Generation
53 LeBron James, e.g.
54 ___ room

BRAINSNACK® **Sweet Thing**

Which candy (1–12) does not belong?

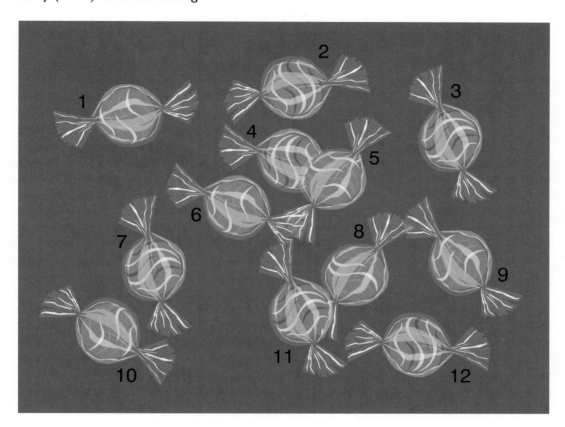

WORD WALL

Beginning at the left side of the wall, make a word by adding one group of letters from each column as you move left to right. When you have found the first word, go back to the second column and start the next word, gathering one group of letters from each column and so on until all the letters are used to make six words.

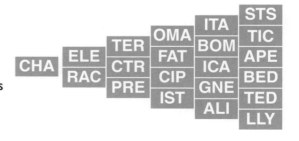

Sport Maze

Draw the shortest way from the ball to the goal. You can only move along vertical and horizontal lines, not along diagonal lines. The figure on each square indicates the number of squares the ball must be moved in the same direction. You can change direction at each stop.

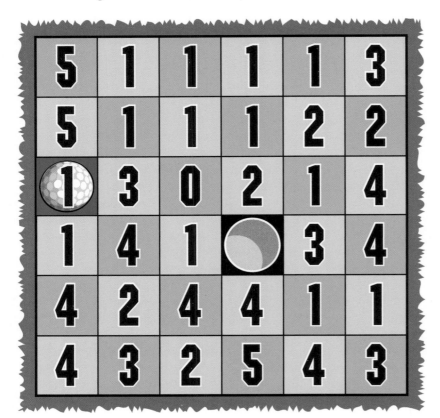

ONE LETTER LESS OR MORE

The word on the right side contains the letters of the word on the left side, plus or minus the letter in the middle. One letter is already in the right place.

P A R I S I A N -A S ☐ ☐ ☐ ☐ ☐

Futoshiki

Fill in the 5 x 5 grid with the numbers from 1 to 5 once per row and column, while following the greater-than/lesser-than symbols shown. There is only one valid solution that can be reached through logic and clear thinking alone!

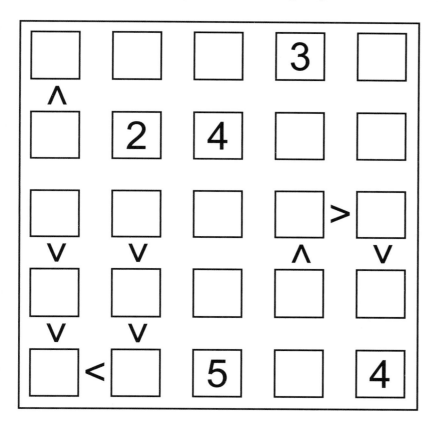

trivia

• Who composed the score for *The Pink Panter?*

LETTERBLOCKS

Move the letterblocks around so that words associated with weather are formed on the top and bottom rows. In some blocks, the letter from the top row has been switched with the letter from the bottom row.

Sudoku

Fill in the grid so that each row, each column, and each 3 x 3 frame contains every number from 1 to 9.

						3		
5				6				1
			8		7		6	
		4	7	8	3			
	1	9	5	4		8		
3	5				6			
				7			4	
2	8	3	4				7	
		7		3		5		

do you KNOW?

Which element makes up around 78% of air?

SYMBOL SUMS

Can you work out these number sums using three of these four symbols? $+ - \div \times$

$$9 \ \square \ 5 \ \square \ 3 \ \square \ 6 = 7$$

CROSSWORD Flags with Circles

ACROSS

1 ___ doble (bullfight music)
5 Gate fastener
10 *Play Bridge* author Sharif
14 Matterhorn's peaks
15 River near Albertville
16 In the buff
17 Asian nation with a circle on its flag
19 CAT ___
20 Dandie Dinmont, for one
21 Sugar pill
23 Appoint
24 Drunk as a skunk
25 Bamboozle
27 Charity ball VIPs
30 Audible exhale
33 Ginger ___
35 Nairobi locale
36 Mount in Deuteronomy
37 In the saddle
39 Knighted actor McKellen
40 Feckless
42 Normandy battle site
43 Sam Cooke's "Chain ___"
44 Looked intently
46 *Dallas* matriarchal name
48 Approached
50 "To your health!"
54 Sleeping car
56 Rockette, for one
57 Jacob's twin
58 U.S. state with a circle on its flag
60 Tear apart
61 Patriot Allen
62 "... ___ my Annabel Lee": Poe
63 Early Iranian
64 Bassoon inserts
65 Father of Deimos

DOWN

1 Cannelloni, e.g.
2 Balm additives
3 San Antonio team
4 Largest living bird
5 Portrait, hopefully
6 Hebrew zither
7 Pharmacist's "three times"
8 Barely moved
9 Doctored
10 Bawdy
11 Balkan state with a circle on its flag
12 Egyptian or Syrian, e.g.
13 Nevada gambling resort
18 Elevated
22 Roused
24 In progress
26 *A Bug's Life* bugs
28 *Saving Private* ___ (1998)
29 Performed an aria
30 Felucca, e.g.
31 One of the Nereids
32 Nordic nation with a circle on its flag
34 It might be hard to swallow
37 Leading players
38 Whale relatives
41 Warm-up
43 Sweet Brown of song
45 Part of a bureau
47 Harpoon metal
49 Matrilineal kin
51 Shankar's strings
52 "___ ear and out..."
53 Keeps an eye on
54 Salon wave
55 Plaintiff
56 Nigeria's neighbor
59 Pronoun for a ship

Fore!

This is a tricky hole at The Masters, with bunkers and water hazards and long grass. If you can get from the tee to the flag without encountering a hazard, you have a Hole in One and are well on your way to being a champion. There is only one route to the pin that avoids the hazards. Each time you pass through a bunker, a water hazard, or long grass, you drop a shot. If you pass through one bunker, your score when you reach the flag is 2. If you encounter two bunkers and a water hazard, your score is 4 and maybe this game is just not for you! The solution shows the Hole in One pathway.

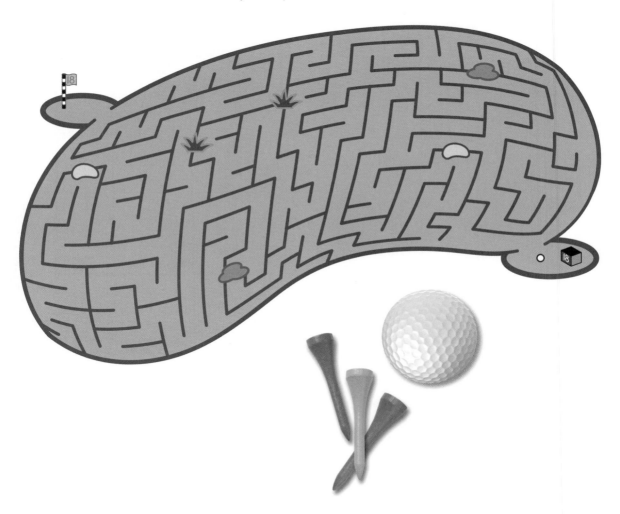

TRIVIAL PURSUIT # Good Grief!

Nearly 70 years ago, on Oct. 2, 1950, Charles M. Schulz's syndicated comic strip Peanuts debuted in seven newspapers nationwide. The last strip (of 17,897) ran Feb. 13, 2000—the day before Schulz died.

TEST YOUR KNOWLEDGE OF GOOD OL' CHARLIE BROWN (SCHULZ'S ALTER EGO) AND THE GANG.

1 Who said "My anxieties have anxieties"?

_____

2 She observed that "Happiness is a warm puppy."

_____

3 Who has a strong attachment to a security blanket?

_____

4 Name Schroeder's favorite composer.

_____

5 Who is the object of Charlie Brown's unrequited love?

_____

6 Name the character Marcie calls "sir."

_____

7 Who was Snoopy's BBF (best bird friend)?

_____

8 How much did Lucy charge for psychiatric help?

_____

9 What WWI flying ace was Snoopy's nemesis?

_____

10 Who walks around in his own dust storm?

_____

11 What character first appeared in 1966 but was not named until four years later.

_____

12 When is Charlie Brown's birthday?

_____

Flags with Stars

ACROSS

1 Sudden ache
5 Take to task
10 Lip disservice
14 Quarter
15 Mirren in *Arthur*
16 Ballet skirt
17 Country with a star on its flag
19 Ancient lyre
20 Time being
21 Mariners' home
23 Twin of Pollux
24 Pumped up
25 Big books
28 Identify with
31 Reclaim
34 Medieval treasure chest
36 "Blowin' in the Wind" singer
37 Starting point for Tiger
38 Standards
40 Like Arctic winds
41 Blofeld in *You Only Live Twice*
44 Business outfit
45 Clouseau's valet
46 Like rap lyrics
48 Tree with gray bark
50 Goose eggs
52 Singer Morissette
56 Pitching gem
58 Deluxe
59 Bake-sale buys
60 Country with a star on its flag
62 Singer Guthrie
63 Harpo Productions founder
64 As a czar, he was terrible
65 Eminem hit
66 Spiteful
67 Rare goose

DOWN

1 High anxiety
2 Carrier Dome, e.g.
3 Salamanders
4 Newspaper name
5 Boardroom VIP
6 Conn's post
7 Stevedore's org.
8 Like a pea-soup fog
9 Evoke affection
10 Lordly
11 Country with a star on its flag
12 Downtown commuter plane
13 "Of course!"
18 Suffix for switch
22 Like sharp cheddar
26 Youngest Greek god
27 Third-stringer
29 Statesmanship
30 War goddess
31 Unit of progress
32 Prefix for space
33 Country with a star on its flag
35 Pierre's date
39 Catfooted
42 Mountie hat
43 Neophyte: Var.
45 Shame
47 It's clipped by the thrifty
49 Jazz singer Laine
51 Buddhist dome
53 Without worldly wisdom
54 From early Peru
55 British weight
56 Health retreats
57 "Sugar Lips" trumpeter
58 Part of QED
61 Vocalized pauses

BRAINSNACK® **More Sweet Things**

Which lollipop (1–7) does not belong?

QUICK CROSSWORD

Place the words listed below in the crossword grid.

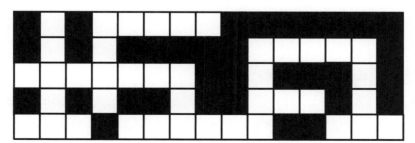

ANGRY TIGHT SERIOUS CLEAR ACID THIN TRUE ILL DRY SUDDEN SAD WET

Word Sudoku

Complete the grid so that each row, each column, and each 3 x 3 frame contains the nine letters from the black box below. The hidden nine-letter word is in the diagonal from top left to bottom right.

A	B	D	F	I	M	N	O	T

		I				O		
					B			D
	N		T	A				M
N	T	O						
				I				
			A			D	T	B
F	O			M		T	I	
I		A			O			N

do you KNOW?

Who narrates
*One Thousand and
One Nights?*

UNCANNY TURN

Rearrange the letters of the phrase below to form a cognate anagram, one that is related or connected in meaning to the original phrase. The answer can be one or more words.

HOT WATER

CROSSWORD Historic Figures

ACROSS

1 He flew with a feather
6 Like ____ out of hell
10 Get ready for
14 *Invisible Cities* author Calvino
15 Moore in *The Joneses*
16 Folk knowledge
17 Three-bean dish
18 Saroyan protagonist
19 Harnesses
20 Holy Roman Empire founder
23 Circus catcher
24 OSS, now
25 Sherwood and Black
29 Contaminate
33 Seafarer's greeting
34 Set up
36 Barely read
37 Midday refresher
38 http://www.yahoo.com, for one
39 Make dangerous
40 Cultivated
42 On-ramp sign
44 Boating on the Baltic
45 Doped up
47 Grief
49 Sp. lady
50 Terrible twoster
51 Last English king to die in battle
60 Not a pretty fruit
61 Japan's first permanent capital
62 Marisa in *The Wrestler*
63 One often seen with braces
64 Scriptural paradise
65 On mom's side
66 Hind's counterpart
67 A scout may do a good one
68 Newton fractions

DOWN

1 Spinal pad
2 Bryce Canyon locale
3 ____ fide (in bad faith)
4 Hogwash
5 Lots and lots
6 Some prosecutors, briefly
7 Friend of Mary Poppins
8 Eastern au pair
9 1994 Van Damme film
10 Trials and tribulations, e.g.
11 Shake a tail
12 Vicinity
13 Hatching post?
21 Suffix for leather
22 Grissom of *CSI*
25 Canines to beware of
26 Windy City terminus
27 Participated in a rodeo event
28 Ink squirter
29 Pharmacy supply
30 Official decree
31 Four for the road
32 Peel and Bovary
35 Yorkshire river
41 Ablution
42 Longed (for)
43 Oasis fruit
44 Hopkins in *The Elephant Man*
46 Madrigal syllable
48 Line to sign
51 Groovy things
52 "____ no respect!": Dangerfield
53 DuVall in *Girl, Interrupted*
54 Miami-____ County
55 Corner a raccoon
56 Crew member
57 Mrs. David Bowie
58 Interconnection of nerves
59 *Tomorrow Never ____* (1997)

Spot the Differences

Find the nine differences in the image on the bottom right.

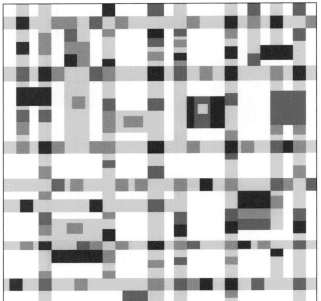

do you KNOW

Where was the
Aztec Empire
based?

trivia

- The film *Cool Runnings*
  features which sport?

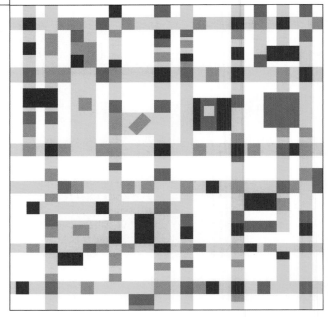

WORD SEARCH — Laboratory

All the words are hidden vertically, horizontally, or diagonally—in both directions. The letters that remain unused form a sentence from left to right.

```
L I T E R A T U R E L A S B S
E C I V R E S E O R A T R O T
R Y R E S S C L E A R C E H L
B I N S E N T A E O T R T S U
A I C C E E S C O B F C L L S
D N O I A L I I S S A B I A E
E R C L C O D D S P A L F I R
P S B L O O D E S M I F N R S
G I L N C G L M E R E A E E T
E S I A N T Y G L N Y I L T S
M N C A T A L Y S T S G P A Y
O R O O T I S S U E G T A M L
N T B L I B N C H O P U P W A
T O X I C O L O G I C A L A N
N E T H E X C R E M E N T R A
E F S T N E M E L E I G H T A
G A I T N S P R O F E S S O R
S T C R S Y R I N G E S I M E
```

- ANALYST
- BIOLOGY
- BLOOD
- BOTTLES
- BOXES
- CAPS
- CATALYSTS
- CHOP UP
- CLONE
- ELEMENTS
- EXCREMENT
- FILTERS
- GOGGLES
- LABELS
- LATIN
- LITERATURE
- MEDICAL
- NEEDLES
- PROCESS
- PROFESSOR
- RAW MATERIALS
- RESULTS
- SAFETY
- SCIENCE
- SERVICE
- SYRINGES
- TESTS
- TISSUE
- TOXICOLOGICAL

Binairo

Complete the grid with zeros and ones until there are 6 zeros and 6 ones in every row and every column. No more than two of the same number can be next to or under each other. Rows or columns with exactly the same content are not allowed. There is only one valid solution.

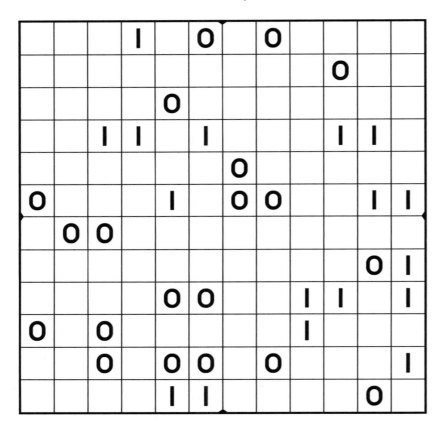

do you KNOW?

Which oceans meet at the Strait of Magellan?

_____

WORD POWER **Back to School**

Sharpen your pencil and put on your thinking cap—it's time to head back to school. We've selected a roster of words that will challenge learners of all ages. Will you make the grade or draw a blank?

· ·

1. **parochial** (puh-'roh-kee-uhl) *adj.*—A: rigorous. B: elementary. C: run by a church.

2. **conscientious** (kon-shee-'en-shuhs) *adj.*—A: extremely careful. B: alert. C: well educated.

3. **pore** (pohr) *v.*—A: quote at length. B: study intently. C: write by hand.

4. **carrel** ('kehr-uhl) *n.*—A: library nook. B: songbook. C: punctuation mark.

5. **curriculum** (kuh-'rih-kyuh-luhm) *n.*—A: lecture hall. B: highest grade. C: set of courses.

6. **pedantic** (pih-'dan-tik) *adj.*—A: misbehaving. B: making a show of knowledge. C: highly poetic.

7. **glean** (gleen) *v.*—A: divide equally. B: erase. C: gather.

8. **rudiments** ('roo-duh-ments) *n.*—A: wrong answers. B: small classes. C: beginner's skills.

9. **syntax** ('sin-tax) *n.*—A: dictionary. B: sentence structure. C: math equation.

10. **semantic** (sih-'man-tik) *adj.*—A: related to meaning in language. B: collegiate. C: in essay form.

11. **pedagogy** ('peh-duh-goh-jee) *n.*—A: art of teaching. B: debate tactic. C: study of children.

12. **syllabus** ('sih-luh-buhs) *n.*—A: word part. B: class outline. C: textbook.

13. **woolgathering** ('wool-ga-thuh-ring) *n.*—A: taking notes. B: memorizing. C: daydreaming.

14. **cognizant** ('cog-nuh-zent) *adj.*—A: engrossed. B: aware. C: automated.

15. **empirical** (im-'peer-ih-kuhl) *adj.*—A: theoretical. B: quick to learn. C: based on observation.

Halloween Fun

ACROSS

1 Seize
5 Visiting a corn ___
9 *Murder, ___ Wrote*
12 Vehicle
13 Paradise
14 "For ___ a jolly good fellow..."
15 Pierce
16 Carving jack-o'-___
18 Floating marker
20 U.S. Supreme Court Associate Justice Kagan
21 Rank in the Navy
24 Last day of the workweek
25 The Importance of ___ Earnest
26 A man's home is ___ castle
27 Large ice fragment
28 Type of bran
29 Academy Award winner Irene ___
33 Unit of energy
34 Gullible local
35 Fancier variety
39 ___ *Street* (kids' show)
40 You ___ Beautiful (2 words)
41 Kiln
42 Trick-or-___ on Halloween night
44 Desire
48 Cry of fright
49 Thought
50 It encircles a castle
51 Streets (abbrev.)
52 Popular Halloween tricolor treat, candy ___
53 Jane Austen novel

DOWN

1 Fuel
2 Track made by a wheel
3 ___ Airlines, former carrier now owned by Southwest Airlines
4 ___ for apples
5 Cantaloupe
6 Call it ___ (2 words)
7 Way to enlightenment
8 Inputs
9 Rip to bits
10. Substance used in dyeing
11 Written report
17 Inventor Whitney
19 Boot brand name
21 ___ and flow
22 Born
23 Formal address
24 In good shape
26 Witch
28 Mined mineral
29 Wearing a ___ on Oct. 31
30 Alias (abbrev.)
31 Sleep stage (abbrev.)
32 Ginger ___
33 Rare or unusual
34 Word of agreement
35 One who goes out socially
36 Made a mistake
37 Onion relatives
38 Washington, D.C., is its capital
39 Astronomer Carl
41 Doozy
43 Altar words
45 CD-___
46 Herd of whales
47 Flight info (abbrev.)

BRAINSNACK® **Rain or Shine**

Which symbol (1–4) should replace the question mark?

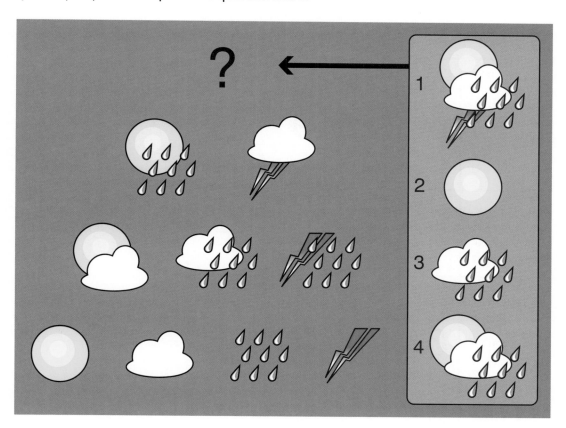

DOUBLETALK

Homophones are words that share the same pronunciation, no matter how they are spelled. If they are spelled differently, then they are called heterographs. Find heterographs meaning:

EXIST and FLYING INSECT

Sudoku X

Fill in the grid so that each row, each column, and each 3 x 3 frame contains every number from 1 to 9. The two main diagonals of the grid also contain every number from 1 to 9.

7						2		
			6	8	5	9		
							8	4
							4	7
		5		3				
					8	1	5	9
			8		7			5
5				2	6			
	7	9	3		1		6	

do you KNOW?

Who sculpted
The Thinker?

BLOCK ANAGRAM

Form the word that is described in the parentheses using the letters above the grid. Extra letters are already in the right place.

DAYDREAMS (2012 Olympic gold medal men's rowing single sculls)

116

CROSSWORD Tricolor Flags

ACROSS

1 "Blame It on the ___ Nova"
6 Food on a skewer
11 "___ Believer": Monkees
14 Like some sanctuaries
15 Maine college town
16 Manx doctor
17 Its flag is red, white, and blue
19 Lennon's Plastic ___ Band
20 Aerosmith's first hit
21 Quack medicine
23 Tear (into)
24 "The ___ Thought of You"
25 Assuaged
29 Insurance type
32 Make ___ for it
33 Hitherto
35 Prefix for graph
36 Put the kibosh on
37 Vroom the engine
38 Interlaken river
39 Abound
41 Went for the gold
43 Renaissance patron
44 Annual fact book
46 Brings to naught
48 Toot one's horn
49 Diddley and Derek
50 Animal that plays dead
53 Soapbox output
57 Coach Holtz
58 Its flag is green, white, and blue
60 Misreckon
61 Nina's mother in *Black Swan*
62 Broom-Hilda's friend
63 DreamWorks ___
64 Of the kidney
65 Maternally related

DOWN

1 R.E.M. or U2
2 Done
3 Cyberspace spot
4 Like North Africa
5 In need of iron
6 City north of 8-Down
7 Time to remember
8 Beethoven's birthplace
9 Phillips ___ Academy
10 Ordered around
11 Its flag is orange, white, and green
12 Choice list
13 Proton's place
18 Ring enclosures
22 Fall preceder, perhaps
25 Stocking stuffer
26 Projecting window
27 Its flag is red, white, and blue
28 Baseless column
29 Expert
30 Winged
31 Harp forerunners
34 Swampland
40 Where Phoenix landed 5/25/08
41 Tobey in *Seabiscuit*
42 Winger in *Terms of Endearment*
43 Miami's time zone
45 Aswan High Dam lake
47 Hockey position
50 Hispanic hurrahs
51 Spam ingredient
52 Chicken chow ___
53 Viva voce
54 Grant Wood's home state
55 "Don't bet ___!"
56 State bird of Hawaii
59 Headphones brand

Fabulously Fashionable

Can you strike a pose with the following round?
It's clearly designed to reveal who's in or out when it comes to being fashion conscious.

1. This heiress-turned-fashion-model is just as comfortable maneuvering the party scene as she is on the runway.

   _____

2. Donna Karan and Marc Jacobs both graduated from this legendary school of design.

   _____

3. Held in New York's Bryant Park, this is the event where top designers from around the world reveal their latest creations.

   _____

4. This reality television program revolved around weekly competitions among young fashion designers.

   _____

5. Which European city stunned the fashion world in 2006 by banning from its runways models with a BMI less than 18?

   _____

6. Which famous music star known as 'Posh Spice' branched out in fashion, launching her own line in 2008?

   _____

7. Katharine Hepburn starred in a 1969 Broadway musical about the life of this French fashion designer who created "the little black dress."

   _____

8. The 1957 musical Funny Face, starring Fred Astaire as the fashion photographer Dick Avery, was a fictional account of the early career of which high-fashion legend?

   _____

9. Which magazine editor's former assistant wrote the book The Devil Wears Prada?

   _____

10. Simon Doonan is the creative director and mastermind window dresser of which fashionable New York shopping destination?

   _____

11. Which famous female designer is renowned for desiging her signature wrap dress.

   _____

12. PETA is trying to change people's minds about wearing these.

   _____

Wax Works

Ivor Wick has a small candlemaking shop where he produces and sells candles of different colors and designs. Every day he makes a batch of different colors and different designs: Last week his theme was chess pieces. How many candles did he make on each of the listed days, and what was the color and design of each batch?

		QUANTITY					COLOR					DESIGN				
		450	500	600	700	750	Green	Orange	Red	White	Yellow	Bishops	Knights	Queens	Pawns	Rooks
DAY	Monday															
	Tuesday															
	Wednesday															
	Thursday															
	Friday															
DESIGN	Bishops															
	Knights															
	Queens															
	Pawns															
	Rooks															
COLOR	Green															
	Orange															
	Red															
	White															
	Yellow															

1. The bishop-shaped candles weren't made on Tuesday, but they were made earlier in the week than the batch of 700 candles.

2. Ivor made 100 more candles in the shape of pawns than the number of yellow candles, which he made on Thursday.

3. The knight-shaped candles were made the day before the green candles and two days before the batch of 500 orange candles.

4. One hundred and fifty more candles in the shape of queens were made than the number of red candles, which he made on Monday.

Themeless 1

ACROSS

1 Eases off nursing
6 Poet Pound
10 Bit of cunning
14 Apportion
15 Become frayed
16 Indigo plant
17 House members
20 Takes off wrongly
21 Home of Gonzaga U.
22 ___ Wee Reese
23 Seed envelope
24 Valley
28 Epithet for Elvis
31 Sailor's "yo!"
32 Sony competitor
34 Huge star
35 Horse transport
36 Salary ceiling
37 Prefix for fauna
38 City S of Moscow
40 Olympic-ring color
42 Cartman's *South Park* pal
43 *Princess* ___ (1994)
45 Tissue claim
47 Scored 100%
48 Boo-___
49 New Mexico capital
52 Bedevil
56 *Avatar* actress
58 "___ magnifique!"
59 Staring sort
60 *CSI* center
61 Like the Kalahari
62 City near Tokyo
63 Furies' number

DOWN

1 Beaver Cleaver's dad
2 "Waiting for the Robert ___"
3 Heidi's home
4 *Beatles for Sale* song
5 Like some headphones
6 Flock females
7 Buddhism branch
8 Sand viper's prey
9 Plains Indian
10 Oahu beach resort
11 Void
12 Property lawyer's concern
13 "What ___ can I say?"
18 Does a slow burn
19 Shredded
24 Anarchy
25 *Appointment in Samarra* author
26 Silver's rider
27 Prefix for iliac
28 Keys in
29 Exploding stars
30 Tiny flash
33 Scots negative
39 Milk sugar
40 Arthur of early TV
41 With zero chance
42 Belly
44 Steady guy
46 Home of Faunus
49 One-time Orly jets
50 Leeds river
51 Companion of Ares
52 Tenderfoot
53 For ___ and a day
54 Hawaiian honker
55 Locust, e.g.
57 Sundown, to Shelley

WEATHER CHART   Sunny

Where will the sun shine? With the knowledge that each arrow points to a place where a symbol should be, can you locate the sunny spots? The symbols cannot be next to each other vertically, horizontally, or diagonally. A symbol cannot be placed on top of an arrow. We show one symbol.

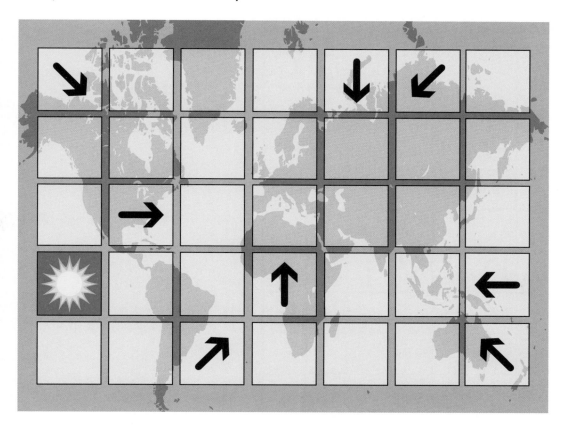

TRIANAGRAM

Three-word groups of anagrams are also called triplets or trianagrams.
Complete the group:

E A S T E R N   _ _ _ _ _ _ _   _ _ _ _ _ _ _

Word Sudoku

Complete the grid so that each row, each column, and each 3 x 3 frame contains the nine letters from the black box below. The hidden nine-letter word is in the diagonal from top left to bottom right.

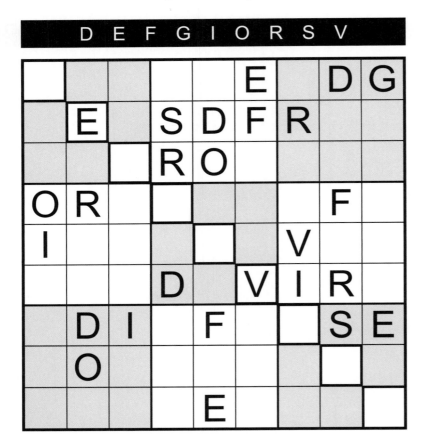

D E F G I O R S V

trivia
- What name is Theodor Geisel better known by?

_____

CROSSWORD Color Coordinated

ACROSS

1 Fill-in at the office
5 *The Dark Knight* director
10 NCOs
14 *Caprica* star Morales
15 Maine college town
16 River to the Caspian Sea
17 *Star Wars* villain in black
19 Highway rig
20 Make good
21 Storm
23 NBA great Greer
24 Ball-___ hammer
25 Winwood in *The Misfits*
29 Pacify
32 Cowardly Lion actor
33 Soothe
35 Public transport
36 France's Belle-___-en-Mer
37 Cobb and Armstrong
38 Apply liniment
39 Pumps up the volume
41 Italian noble
43 Take bad news badly
44 Arid to the max
46 Sanctioned
48 "Keeper of sheep" in Genesis
49 Fuel up, in a way
50 Paul in *Casablanca*
53 Shake up
57 West End opener
58 Holiday figure in red and white
60 Daphne on *Frasier*
61 11-year-old, for one
62 Fumbles the ball, e.g.
63 *Brokeback Mountain* heroine
64 Concerning
65 Hockey feint

DOWN

1 *Bill & ___ Bogus Journey* (1991)
2 Duped twin in Genesis
3 Staal of the NHL
4 Ace of diamonds?
5 *Billy Budd,* e.g.
6 Towards the mouth
7 Israeli airport
8 Work without ___ (risk it)
9 1965 Beatles song
10 Person of interest
11 Superhero in emerald and black
12 Highland hats
13 Squint-eyed opening
18 Do a physician's job
22 "Give ___ break!"
25 Walter ___ Disney
26 Hayek in *Grown Ups*
27 Superhero in purple
28 Brand or John
29 Fettuccine, e.g.
30 Moleskin color
31 Set in deeply
34 Indy driver St. James
40 Teenage witch Spellman
41 Flockhart of *Ally McBeal*
42 Exquisite
43 Blotchy
45 Tribe also called the Arikara
47 Secular
50 W Syrian city
51 One of the life sciences: Abbr.
52 First light
53 Solar disk
54 River at Bern
55 Istanbul native
56 Latin 101 verb
59 Alumna identifier

Number Series

What figure needs to be erased in order to respect the underlying logic of the series of figures?

LETTER LINE

Put a letter in each of the squares below to make a word related to writing.
The number clues refer to other words that can be made from the whole.

5 6 7 7 8 4 SOLDIERS • 2 10 6 9 1 2 4 POSSIBLY
4 9 1 8 10 FORM • 4 2 10 1 6 THROWING WEAPON • 2 9 3 5 3 4 SNAPSHOTS

1	2	3	4	5	6	7	8	9	10

Sudoku

Fill in the grid so that each row, each column, and each 3 x 3 frame contains every number from 1 to 9.

								8
	1							
9		6			2			
6			7					2
		2			4		9	5
4	5			3			7	6
	2		4	9	6	3		
5		3	8			6	4	1
	6		3	1				

do you KNOW?

The Brenner Pass goes through which mountains?

SYMBOL SUMS

Can you work out these number sums using three of these four symbols? $+ \; - \; \div \; \times$

$$16 \; \square \; 8 \; \square \; 2 \; \square \; 2 = 11$$

Themeless 2

ACROSS

1 Lavender
6 1, on the Mohs scale
10 Ballet's Odette, alternatively
14 Top-drawer
15 All-inclusive abbr.
16 Calling
17 Dog that originated in Wales
20 Burrito cousins
21 Spirited, in a sense
22 Mother hog
23 Long in *The Best Man*
24 Hoodwinked
28 Caroline Wozniacki's homeland
32 Change for a five
33 Took the plunge
35 Gray of *Buck Rogers*
36 Aggie, for one
37 2012 Demi Moore film
38 Roman 1,101
39 *Mad* cartoonist Drucker
41 Insomniac's desire
43 Lo-cal
44 Bedlam or worse
46 Claims formally
48 Persian Gulf federation
49 ___ adjudicata
50 Mini "ha-ha!"
54 Hippie era
58 Game with rails
60 With the wherewithal
61 Suffix for switch
62 *Pinky* star Jeanne
63 Fly like an eagle
64 Drubbing
65 *Golden Boy* playwright

DOWN

1 "___ we forget ..."
2 Endoscopy focuses
3 Neeson in *Ethan Frome*
4 Country albums?
5 Sri Lanka, formerly
6 Holistic remedies
7 Chase robot
8 Latticework strip
9 Scrubbed
10 Smith is a common one
11 Habeas corpus, e.g.
12 *The African Queen* screenwriter
13 Geekazoid
18 Used an axe
19 Be the end of
24 Cause for pause
25 Scallion
26 Sheena's mount
27 Dawdle
28 Removed a word
29 Mueller-Stahl in *Shine*
30 Sent through a sieve
31 Makes booties
34 Lobster coral
40 Cabdriver
41 Cover
42 Imminent danger
43 Skulking coward
45 Birthday dessert
47 Chihuahua locale
50 IRS functionaries
51 Boxcar resident
52 Campus near Beverly Hills
53 Tortosa's river
54 Mail drop
55 "Dies ___" (hymn)
56 Cut or stet
57 Common IDs
59 Note from a loser

WORD SEARCH Hair Salon

All the words are hidden vertically, horizontally, or diagonally—in both directions. The letters that remain unused form a sentence from left to right.

```
D U S L R U C B R I N Y G E A
B L E A C H P A E R A M A V N
E O N T W A V L E R E B R A B
T U H E H A I D P R I S T H R
R S E A T E T S D N E E H S W
O E I T H E R F F U R D N A D
R A S H A I R S T Y L E A T S
R L T S A T H A T C O N R N T
I N E H T A G L I N S O A O R
M A G A Z I N E S L H I O R A
T B O F A M O D M S O H N I I
I A M A N D L O P I S S O G G
A P P O I N T M E N T A T N H
H A T S C I S S O R S F W I T
B A R B E R C H A I R O C L A
N O I T O L U S E S R T H R E
O O P M A H S H A C I R T U O
S W E T R E A T M E N T L C L
```

- APPOINTMENT
- BALD
- BARBER
- BARBER CHAIR
- BLEACH
- COMB
- CROWN
- CURLING IRON
- CURLS
- DANDRUFF
- FASHION
- GOSSIP
- HAIRSPRAY
- HAIRSTYLE
- LONG
- LOTION
- LOUSE
- MAGAZINES
- MIRROR
- MODEL
- SCISSORS
- SHAMPOO
- SHAVE
- SHEEN
- SHORT
- STRAIGHT
- TEASE
- TREATMENT

Sport Maze

Draw the shortest way from the ball to the goal. You can only move along vertical and horizontal lines, not along diagonal lines. The figure on each square indicates the number of squares the ball must be moved in the same direction. You can change direction at each stop.

4	3	2	4	4	3
5	3	⚪	1	4	1
3	2	3	0	3	1
3	3	1	0	2	5
4	4	4	3	3	3
1	4	5	5	2	2

trivia

- What is Tiger Woods' real name?

ONE LETTER LESS OR MORE

The word on the right side contains the letters of the word on the left side, plus or minus the letter in the middle. One letter is already in the right place.

E D U C T I O N +R ☐ ☐ T ☐ ☐ ☐ ☐ ☐

128

WORD SEARCH   Thanks a Lot

These words represent some of life's many blessings. They are hidden vertically, horizontally, or diagonally—in both directions.

U	F	T	U	Z	P	H	W	H	B	P	Y	H	V	K	K	Y	N	E
X	I	H	Q	E	O	O	T	T	B	L	H	V	Z	M	R	W	B	U
S	B	F	A	M	R	I	N	R	P	L	P	L	W	N	R	N	P	J
M	W	C	E	P	A	N	V	A	D	X	C	R	W	W	H	L	G	Q
R	E	C	E	F	M	O	X	E	N	U	B	O	O	K	S	M	Y	V
K	P	U	P	U	S	I	K	H	S	K	L	J	Q	Y	E	H	X	H
P	G	O	S	P	M	T	S	N	X	L	G	A	V	I	I	M	I	E
L	L	I	L	O	I	A	K	I	R	R	Y	Y	U	V	Y	S	I	A
L	C	A	S	I	L	C	G	H	A	Q	X	G	S	G	Y	M	O	L
N	B	G	P	C	E	U	Y	Q	S	E	X	F	L	Q	H	Z	Z	T
Z	R	H	O	C	S	D	O	E	I	T	L	V	Z	B	H	T	N	H
T	R	A	V	E	T	E	W	W	I	E	F	H	R	E	T	Y	E	L
H	Y	G	R	E	N	E	B	M	G	A	X	T	E	A	K	G	D	R
H	X	K	Y	V	W	I	E	D	E	V	O	L	T	U	R	S	V	Z
R	M	A	H	O	H	X	H	S	R	F	P	X	A	T	S	S	G	T
N	K	F	R	I	E	N	D	S	H	H	L	A	W	Y	B	X	S	Z
N	Q	K	J	D	O	O	F	V	N	F	A	M	I	L	Y	C	Z	B
D	R	E	A	M	S	S	T	E	P	U	X	L	I	F	E	J	L	F
P	E	T	J	X	U	E	R	R	W	Y	S	Q	Y	J	P	N	C	E

- ART
- BEAUTY
- BOOKS
- DREAMS
- EARTH
- EDUCATION
- ENERGY
- FAITH
- FAMILY
- FOOD
- FRIENDS
- HEALTH
- HOME
- LAUGHTER
- LIFE
- LOVE
- MUSIC
- PEACE
- PETS
- SMILES
- SUNSHINE
- TIME
- WATER
- WORK

Keep Going

Start on a blank square of your choice and connect as many blank squares as possible with one single continuous line. You can only connect squares along vertical and horizontal lines, not along diagonal lines. You must continue the connecting lineup until the next obstacle, i.e., the border of the box, a black square, or a square that has already been used. You can change direction at any obstacle you meet. Each square can only be used once. The number of blank squares that will be left unused is marked in the upper square. There is more than one solution. We only show one solution.

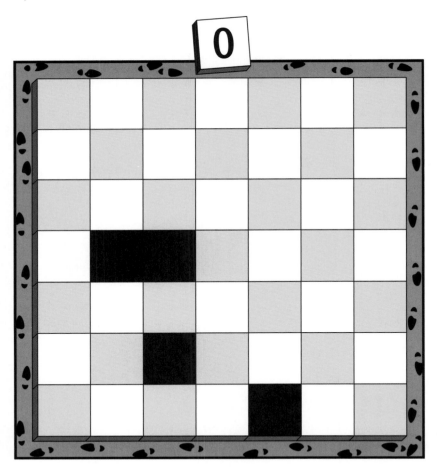

Binairo

Complete the grid with zeros and ones until there are 5 zeros and 6 ones in every row and every column. No more than two of the same number can be next to or under each other. Rows or columns with exactly the same content are not allowed. There is only one valid solution.

		0			1				
	1	1			0		1		
								0	
	0				1		0		
	1	1				1			
1								0	
		1	1				1		
0	1			1			1		
		0							
0	1				1				
		0				0	0		

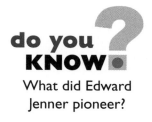

do you KNOW?

What did Edward Jenner pioneer?

_____

TRIANAGRAM

Three-word groups of anagrams are also called triplets or trianagrams.
Complete the group:

LOOP _ _ _ _   _ _ _ _

Famous Hotels

ACROSS

1 Inferno
5 Number on a tag
10 Two-stick drumbeat
14 ____-Day vitamins
15 More secret
16 Broad-topped hill
17 Hôtel de Paris site
19 "____ can you see ..."
20 First-born
21 Lost city of gold
23 Tongue jewelry
25 Dice throw
26 Gathered
30 Sears
33 H, to Hellenes
34 Brief review
36 Act component
37 Pipsqueak
39 Keeps for later
41 Twelfth Jewish month
42 Religious cup
44 Metric volume
46 "Maid of Athens, ____ we part": Byron
47 Group of nine
49 Wanders idly
51 Two make a sextet
53 *Young Frankenstein* heroine
54 Cabbage cousin
57 Iran, until 1935
61 Outstanding
62 Breidenbacher Hof site
64 Cook crayfish
65 Swiss border lake
66 Swan genus
67 "Bliss" singer Tori
68 Schlosshotel Hugenpoet site
69 Forbidden thing

DOWN

1 Where the heart is
2 Carbonic compound
3 Do a banker's job
4 Breaking news
5 Snaps
6 Genetic carrier
7 As to
8 Prison chambers
9 Weakens
10 Hotel Lungarno site
11 Chateau Marmont site
12 *Diary of ____ Housewife* (1970)
13 Rochester clinic
18 Poly follower
22 Sheep genus
24 Transfer image
26 Entrance-ramp sign
27 Policy flip-flop
28 Omni La Mansion del Rio Hotel site
29 Nautical crane
31 Acclimate
32 Tennis star Monica
35 Culture dish
38 Male falcons
40 *All the King's Men* star
43 Of the flock
45 Double star in Orion
48 Google tribute logo
50 Inmate's dream
52 Turns on an axis
54 Rum cake
55 Leeway
56 Credos
58 Fly alone
59 Soldering tool
60 Ethnic hairstyle
63 Oil-can letters

BRAINSNACK® Bargain Hunter

Which two letters are missing on the discount card?

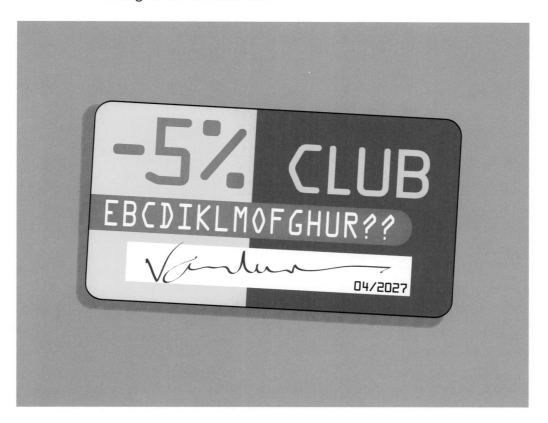

DOODLE PUZZLE

A doodle puzzle is a combination of images, letters, and/or numbers that represent a word or a concept. If you cannot solve a doodle puzzle, do not look at the answer right away. Think hard—and outside the box.

Kakuro

Each number in a black area is the sum of the numbers that you have to enter in the next empty boxes. The empty boxes that make up the sum are called a run. The sum of the across run is written above the diagonal in the black area, and the sum of the down run is written below the diagonal. Runs can only contain the numbers 1 through 9, and each number in a run can only be used once. The gray boxes only contain odd numbers and the white only even numbers.

trivia

- Who was The Beatles' original drummer?

CROSSWORD Two Sopranos

ACROSS

1 *Runaway* ___ (1999)
6 Ticket part
10 Preserve
14 Elton John song
15 Hawaiian harbor
16 *Bus Stop* playwright
17 Roughly
18 Pizzazz
19 *The Sum of All Fears* hero
20 "Kiss Me in the Rain" singer
23 Beirut locale: Abbr.
24 Summer hrs.
25 Ask earnestly
29 Designers
33 "Omigosh!"
34 Like pretzels
36 Tights shade
37 Cousin of "ruff!"
38 Prefix for natal
39 French monarch
40 Be rife with
42 Fanzine subjects
44 Devoted following
45 River feeders
47 Endearing
49 Unit of conductance
50 Major airport
51 Tony Soprano actor
60 Au courant
61 Twin in Genesis
62 Greek physician
63 Orderly
64 Nary a soul
65 Of Nordic stock
66 Dr. Octavius in *Spider-Man 2*
67 Part of QED
68 Harvests

DOWN

1 Spill the beans
2 "Somebody" singer McEntire
3 Novello in *Gosford Park*
4 Hit a two-bagger
5 Principal menu item
6 "___ Leaving Home": Beatles
7 Fight with a knight
8 Suffix for gland
9 Beyond arid
10 Alley in *Look Who's Talking*
11 "Caribbean Blue" singer
12 *Life in London* author
13 Hang fire
21 Simple skills
22 Suffix for ideal
25 Outscores
26 Swamp bird
27 Comparatively risk-free
28 Results of deals
29 Lagoon encloser
30 Third-stringer
31 News Group pest
32 Hotel accommodation
35 Heavenly lion
41 Keepsake
42 Comedienne Coca
43 Greenwich Village neighbor
44 Hack's charge
46 Masseuse's feedback
48 Inelegant
51 Hera's Roman counterpart
52 In ___ (miffed)
53 Castle circler
54 Zither's forerunner
55 Visitor in *Star Trek: DS9*
56 "Heart and Soul" is one
57 Kovalchuk of the NHL
58 One of the tides
59 Country hotels

Check This

The counters on this checkerboard pattern have been moved from their original positions. Each counter has been moved three squares horizontally, vertically, or a mixture of the two (e.g. two up, one right). What appropriate word can be revealed by deducing their original positions? To make things a little harder, two of the counters are red herrings.

do you KNOW?

What are the names of the four members of ABBA?

_____

_____

_____

_____

Horoscope

Fill in the grid so that every row, every column and every frame of six boxes contains six different symbols: health, work, money, happiness, family and love. Look at the row or column that corresponds with your sign of the zodiac, and find out which of the six symbols are important for you today. The symbols appear in increasing order of importance (1–6). It's up to you to translate the meaning of each symbol to your specific situation.

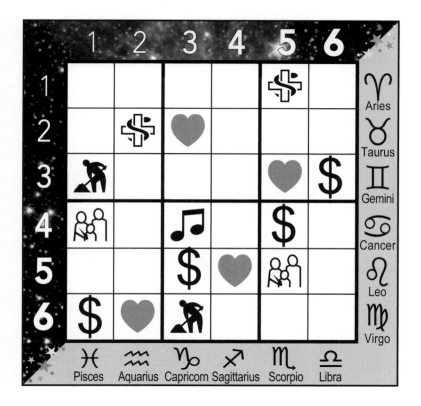

delete ONE

Delete one letter from

CLEAR DARLINGS

and rearrange the rest to find a pin-up.

_____

_____

FRIENDS

What do the following words have in common?

LIST GUARD FLY BOARD BIRD BERRIES LEG MAIL

By Leaps and Bounds

ACROSS

1 French mustard
6 Elapsed
10 Bonneville Flats site
14 "It's ___ bet!"
15 Make eyes at
16 LaBeouf of *Disturbia*
17 2008 Stallone film
18 Sadie Hawkins Day times
20 Currently of interest
22 String quartet member
23 General ___ chicken
24 Go brunette
25 Voiceless
28 Walks through water
32 NBA's "Big Baby" Davis
33 Like the Oregon Trail
35 Window ledge
36 Act the straggler
37 "Honey ___": Beatles
38 Bubba Watson's org.
39 Load to bear
41 Mounds
43 Political slant
44 Joined the dark side
46 Reaching a high
48 British isle
49 Aid an arsonist
50 Drunken states
54 Group within a group
57 Sidewalk game
59 Fall shade
60 Not fooled by
61 "Take Me" singer White
62 Pricker
63 "Us" singer Celine
64 French cathedral city
65 Sorts

DOWN

1 Tavern missile
2 Japanese golfer Aoki
3 Act too hastily
4 "Pretty Woman" singer Roy
5 One who has turned right?
6 Gallup sampling
7 It comes before beauty
8 Pole or Czech
9 Halfheartedly
10 Good for nothing
11 Spicy cuisine
12 Brings to light
13 Shakespeare's own
19 Rock-the-baby toy
21 Saudi province
25 Visibly happy
26 Wright Brothers invention
27 Love god
28 Precipitous
29 Bunny bounce
30 Marbles in the British Museum
31 Street language
34 Previous to
40 Tut, to Nefertiti
41 Weekly business expense
42 Ex-Patriot Junior
43 Lacking details
45 Common-interest group
47 Costello's straight man
50 Did a farrier's job
51 Collette in *About a Boy*
52 "I've had it ___ here!"
53 Sugarland hit
54 Leg bone
55 French father
56 Coastal eagles
58 ___-Magnon man

BRAIN FITNESS # Number Fun 2

Every row and column contains a +, −, and x, and ends with a different total number between 20 and 28 inclusive. Can you complete the grid?

4		11	−	29			=	23
x						x		
10			−	8	x		=	
		−						
	+	3			−	22	=	
+		+						
8		5		53		40	=	
=		=		=		=		
26								

trivia

- In what year was *Friends* first broadcast?

_____

DOODLE PUZZLE

A doodle puzzle is a combination of images, letters, and/or numbers that represent a word or a concept. If you cannot solve a doodle puzzle, do not look at the answer right away. Think hard—and outside the box.

Sudoku

Fill in the grid so that each row, each column, and each 3 x 3 frame contains every number from 1 to 9.

		1				6		
	9				8	7		
	6					5	7	
5	2			9	7	3		8
	8		2	5				
			7	8				
	5		4					
2	7	8	6		5	1	4	9

do you KNOW?

What is named after King Harald I of Denmark?

SYMBOL SUMS

Can you work out these number sums using three of these four symbols? $+ \; - \; \div \; \times$

17 ☐ 8 ☐ 16 ☐ 2 = 72

CROSSWORD · Devilish Roles

ACROSS

1 Broadway backgrounds
5 Sly's *First Blood* role
10 Cast-of-thousands
14 Intensely
15 Arabian aristocrat
16 Aloe ___
17 Devil player in *Ghost Rider*
19 "Go Tell ___ the Mountain"
20 Burdensome
21 Driver's Ed driver
23 Half a diameter
24 Period following Passover
25 Roof problem
27 Santa's reindeer
30 Split rattan
33 Buddhist monks
35 Barcelona bull
36 Half of CIV
37 Zig partner
38 Master Melvin of baseball
39 Foot part
41 Charles in *Gaslight*
43 Furniture chain
44 Moor of Venice
46 Sea swallow
48 Draft status
49 Dracula's bed
53 TV's ___ *Place*
56 Mad cow ___
57 Latin infinitive
58 Voice of Satan on *South Park*
60 Mine, to Michelle
61 Cosmetics mogul Lauder
62 2009 *Star Trek* villain
63 Look after
64 Feats of derring-do
65 Turgenev Museum site

DOWN

1 Sweetness or sourness, e.g.
2 *The Vampire Diaries* heroine
3 Conveyed
4 Infecund
5 Turndown
6 "Bliss" singer Tori
7 Troops
8 They're made by a maid
9 Loud speakers?
10 Plain as day
11 Devil player in *Bedazzled*
12 Club for Rickie Fowler
13 Quitter's word
18 Dissolute one
22 Thurman of *Dangerous Liaisons*
26 Musical buzzer
27 Brewster of *Criminal Minds*
28 "Symphony in Black" artist
29 *The Godfather* composer
30 TV ad award
31 "If it ___ broke ..."
32 Devil player in *The Witches of Eastwick*
34 New Jersey cape
40 Paul in *Now, Voyager*
41 Detonated
42 Cookbook contents
43 Satanic place
45 Bert Lahr's sign, aptly
47 Edwin Drood's fiancée
50 Pretender
51 Rhone tributary
52 Perfumery oil
53 Packinghouse product
54 Elizabeth Reaser's *Twilight* role
55 Dublin language
56 Like Lucy's red hair
59 Hot time in Paris

Missing Stats

Which diagram (1–4) should replace the question mark?

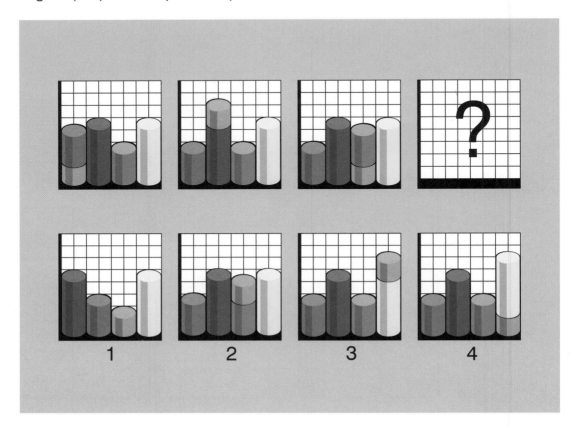

WORD WALL

Beginning at the left side of the wall, make a word by adding one group of letters from each column as you move left to right. When you have found the first word, go back to the second column and start the next word, gathering one group of letters from each column and so on until all the letters are used to make six words.

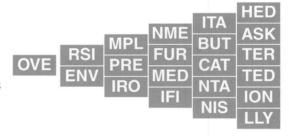

Futoshiki

Fill in the 5 x 5 grid with the numbers from 1 to 5 once per row and column, while following the greater-than/lesser-than symbols shown. There is only one valid solution that can be reached through logic and clear thinking alone!

			5	
	3			
	>	∧	∧	
	2		∨	
>	>	>		3

trivia

- Who played Norman Bates in *Psycho*?

LETTERBLOCKS

Move the letterblocks around so that words associated with rank are formed on the top and bottom rows. In some blocks, the letter from the top row has been switched with the letter from the bottom row.

Antarctica

All the words are hidden vertically, horizontally, or diagonally—in both directions. The letters that remain unused form a sentence from left to right.

```
T E C O N T I N E N T H Y E T
H I R C G O V E R N M E N T K
S E I E C E Y S L I S S O F C
S L A P H T O Y S D N A L S I
N A A N A P A T T S S C O T T
A R C E I B S N T N I G C N C
A R R E S A M O P O R L E E R
S T E I O N I T M I T A S S E
N L V C L S N K S T I C N D T
E A T P A D E N O A A I E N N
D B Y E T R R A U T E E C U I
P O E N E O A L T S S R I M W
M C K G D J L P H R I S T A A
O R R U C F S E P A O N F T I
S O I I F A L D O L P H I N S
S L L N T H E I L O R C R E S
E I L S L A O C E P O N D T U
S E L A H W H E W O P R L D R
```

- AMUNDSEN
- ATMOSPHERE
- COAL
- COAST
- COBALT
- COLONY
- CONTINENT
- DAVIS BAY
- DOLPHINS
- DRIFT ICE
- FJORDS
- FOSSILS
- GLACIERS
- GOVERNMENT
- ISLANDS
- ISOLATED
- KRILL
- MINERALS
- MOSSES
- ORES
- PENGUINS
- PLANKTON
- POLAR STATIONS
- PORPOISE
- RUSSIA
- SCOTT
- SEALS
- SOUTH POLE
- TREATY
- WHALE
- WINTER

Word Pyramid

Each word in the pyramid has the letters of the word above it, plus a new letter.

S
(1) to the same degree
(2) pitiful
(3) serious disease of the immune system
(4) thoughts
(5) suggest
(6) infests
(7) disappeared

do you **KNOW**

Which semiaquatic Australian mammal lays eggs?

_____

Fore!

This is a tricky hole at The Masters, with bunkers and water hazards and long grass. If you can get from the tee to the flag without encountering a hazard, you have a Hole in One and are well on your way to being a champion. There is only one route to the pin that avoids the hazards. Each time you pass through a bunker, a water hazard, or long grass, you drop a shot. If you pass through one bunker, your score when you reach the flag is 2. If you encounter two bunkers and a water hazard, your score is 4 and maybe this game is just not for you! The solution shows the Hole in One pathway.

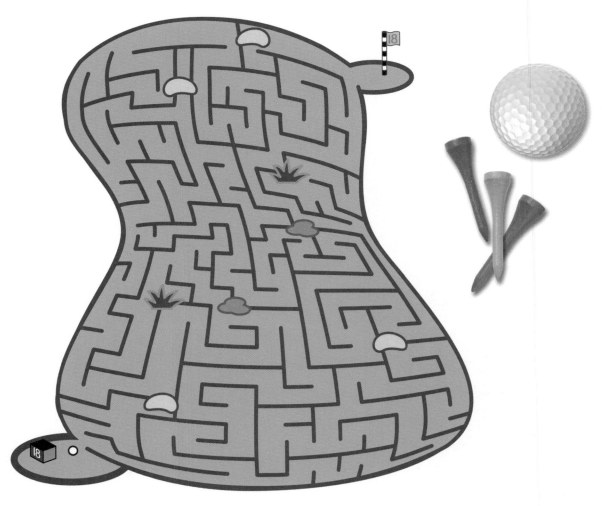

CROSSWORD **Artistic Roles**

ACROSS

1 43,560 square feet
5 Burrito topping
10 Sixties do
14 Dominant
15 Fanzine subjects
16 Crashing bore
17 2011 François Rostain role
19 Rehab target
20 *South Pacific* sailors
21 Rode a float, say
23 Fleur-de-___
24 Inner Hebrides island
25 Instants
29 Goof-off
32 Year in Spain
33 Flower leaf
35 Anne in *The Longshot*
36 Lays down the lawn
38 Israeli Peace Nobelist
40 Snub
41 College credits
43 Fishing spot
45 Kind of monitor
46 Slip
48 Macaw and parakeet, e.g.
50 Take a giant step
51 Follower of yoo
52 Scotland's national flower
55 Flair
59 Jay or Bill of golf
60 2012 Bill Hader role
62 Avonlea girl
63 Obsessively pursue
64 From here to eternity
65 Sortie
66 Great Lakes mnemonic
67 Shane Battier's alma mater

DOWN

1 City in Iowa
2 Suffix for motor
3 Baltic port
4 Authorize
5 Neatly avoid
6 Sports drinks
7 Captain's journal
8 Invitation to a duel
9 Storm
10 Makes progress
11 2002 Salma Hayek role
12 Houston university
13 Opinion page
18 Holds one's horses
22 Traipse
25 Conductor Kurt
26 Down ___ knee
27 2004 Andy Garcia role
28 Glasses
29 The arms of Morpheus
30 Spew forth
31 South African coins
34 Abbr. at JFK
37 Emphasized
39 Seattle team
42 Word with bucket or hot
44 Coin of Stockholm
47 Cannonball dive sound
49 Complained like Simba
52 "___ she blows!"
53 *The English Patient* heroine
54 Opposite of exo-
55 Greene's "quiet American"
56 ___ En-lai
57 Gander's remark
58 Ultimatum word
61 One side of a reservoir

Sport Maze

Draw the shortest way from the ball to the goal. You can only move along vertical and horizontal lines, not along diagonal lines. The figure on each square indicates the number of squares the ball must be moved in the same direction. You can change direction at each stop.

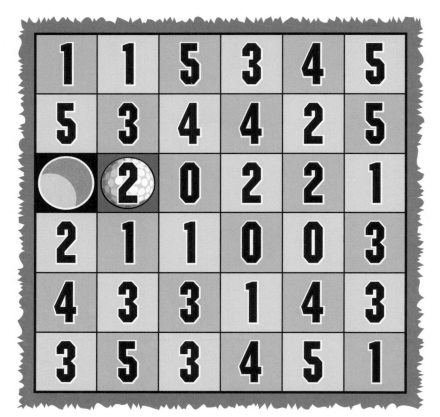

do you KNOW

Which country won the first soccer World Cup?

ONE LETTER LESS OR MORE

The word on the right side contains the letters of the word on the left side, plus or minus the letter in the middle. One letter is already in the right place.

N A T U R I S T +T A ☐ ☐ ☐ ☐ ☐ ☐ ☐ ☐

148

TRIVIA QUIZ # Space, the Final Frontier

Set a course for adventure and test your knowledge of deep space with this quick round of questions.

1. What was the American astronaut Alan B. Shepard Jr.'s unique achievement?

2. Christa McAuliffe died when the *Challenger* exploded. What kind of spaceship was it?

3. Around 1900, astronomer Percival Lowell thought he saw what on the surface of Mars?

4. What rocket was used to launch the *Apollo* moon missions in the 1960s and 1970s?

5. Which country launched the first satellite?

6. What was the first living creature sent into space?

7. What name is given to the course of an object circling a planet or the sun?

8. Soviet cosmonaut Valentina Tereshkova achieved what first for her country on June 16, 1963?

9. What was the name of the first space shuttle?

10. Which Apollo mission went disastrously wrong, resulting in the famous radio transmission: "Houston, we've had a problem"?

11. What was the name of the U.S. space probe launched toward Jupiter in 1989?

12. What is the name of Doctor Who's home planet?

13. What is the largest planet in our solar system?

Futoshiki

Fill in the 5 x 5 grid with the numbers from 1 to 5 once per row and column, while following the greater-than/lesser-than symbols shown. There is only one valid solution that can be reached through logic and clear thinking alone!

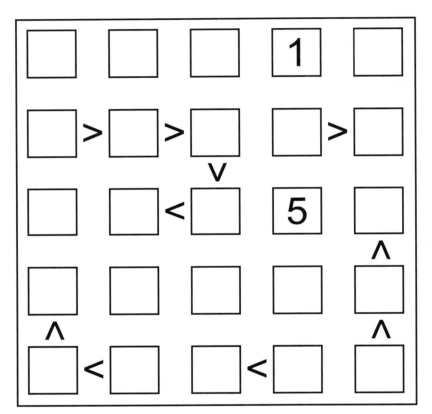

LETTERBLOCKS

Move the letterblocks around so that words associated with the extremes are formed on the top and bottom rows.

AULEFIR

UECSSCS

CROSSWORD Themeless 3

ACROSS

1 Impressionists
6 2001 Dennis Hopper film
10 One of those things
14 *Frolic* composer
15 Archeological shelter
16 Longest Swiss river
17 Province named by Queen Victoria
20 Not religious
21 Finer points
22 Color of Mao's little book
23 Disappear, as a snowman
24 Smear-sheet topic
28 Force out of office
31 Fugitive flights
32 Sooner State city
34 Spartan walkway
35 Sun or moon
36 Narrow inlet
37 Under the weather
38 Gurgling sound
40 Ford, to Chrysler
42 Straight man in comedy
43 Comforted
45 Rhythm
47 Gray and Candler
48 Bygone airline
49 Rochester river
52 "Bird" Parker
56 *Moon Over Parador* star
58 Coldplay's "___ Love"
59 *Billy Budd* captain
60 Aida's native land
61 Mae in *My Little Chickadee*
62 Irish Gaelic
63 "Maybe, Yes" singer Mandell

DOWN

1 Wall Street whizzes
2 Dermal opening
3 Dane of *Grey's Anatomy*
4 "Many happy ___!"
5 Put on a happy face
6 MGM film lion
7 *Modern Family* network
8 Jab
9 Quandary
10 Wrapped food
11 Lodgings
12 Seed cover
13 Earl Grey and Lady Grey
18 1978 Peace Nobelist
19 School on the Rio Grande
24 Plods through
25 *Monte ___* (2011)
26 911 vehicles
27 Sensational
28 Stern with a Strad
29 Baby's distress
30 Berry in *X-Men: The Last Stand*
33 Tyler who was Arwen Undómiel
39 Single or double
40 Self-control
41 Woodworking machine
42 Scared
44 Durango abode
46 The Rock's first name
49 Enlarge
50 ___ *kleine Nachtmusik*
51 Tributary of the Fulda
52 Manitoba tribe
53 Grease job
54 "The devil ___ the details"
55 Morales of *Resurrection Blvd.*
57 OR personnel

Credit Rating

Which number is missing on the bottom credit card?

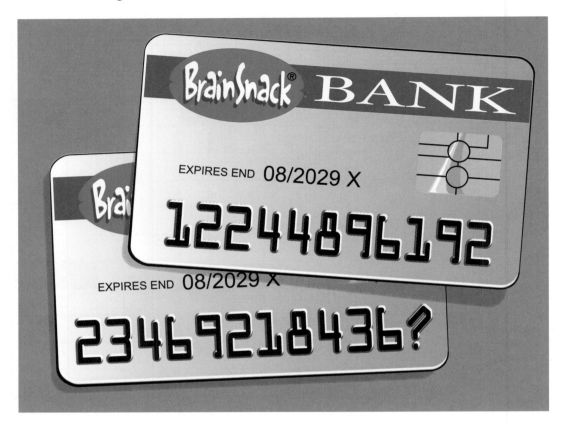

BLOCK ANAGRAM

Form the word that is described in the parentheses using the letters above the grid. Extra letters are already in the right place.

BEE WALL (largest living mammal on earth)

		U			**H**		

CROSSWORD **In the Pink**

ACROSS

1 "____ the Rainbow"
5 Pentacle
9 Songwriter's org.
14 Negri in *Madame Bovary*
15 Dunce cap, for one
16 Weighing machine
17 Pink *Dumbo* paraders
19 Evans in *The Avengers*
20 Parsonage
21 Canada's largest city
23 Mary in *The Maltese Falcon*
24 Kedrova in *Zorba the Greek*
25 *Anthem* author Ayn
28 Cash-back deals
31 Party in Pretoria: Abbr.
34 *Key____* (1948)
36 *Love Story* author Segal
37 Jacob's first wife
39 Hibiscus, for one
41 Trendy London area
42 Internet access
44 Sand hills
46 Straight away
47 Biscotti flavoring
49 Morse clicks
51 Cruise ship deck
52 "____ of do or die ..."
56 Nabisco cracker
59 Magazine for moms
61 "Shaft" singer Hayes
62 Pink birds
64 Formal fiats
65 Drink too much
66 Medieval drudge
67 Stand in the studio
68 Arch over
69 River next to Hades

DOWN

1 Covent Garden staging
2 Ratlike rodents
3 Put in office
4 Bird of prey
5 Capone facial feature
6 Curtis in *The Great Race*
7 Industrious insect
8 Lie in a hammock
9 Give credit to
10 Honors students
11 Pink flower
12 Dismounted
13 Uruguayan coin
18 Hourly
22 Hurrah for José
26 Gripe constantly
27 *Judge____* (Stallone film)
28 3 minutes of boxing
29 Pining oread
30 Tell partner
31 ____ mater
32 Glitzy light
33 Pink cars
35 Serengeti antelope
38 Look before you leap
40 ____ Breeze cocktail
43 Insurance category
45 Hokkaido volcano
48 Forever and a day
50 Parts of acts
53 Woody Allen theme
54 Unemotional
55 County in England
56 Fries or slaw, e.g.
57 Global area
58 Juvenile salamanders
59 "____ Don't Preach": Madonna
60 Paula Cole album
63 Cut off

American Graffiti

Director George Lucas' first financially successful film, *American Graffiti*, debuted in August 1973. The movie, a coming-of-age film celebrating teenage angst, hot rods, drive-ins and rock 'n' roll, accelerated many acting careers.

CAN YOU NAME THESE STARS FROM THE SHOW?

1 Class president Steve Bolander who played by a redhead whose next big acting job was on *Happy Days*.

_____

2 Before he became Han Solo, this bit actor/carpenter performed the pivotal role of Bob Falfa in a '55 Chevy.

_____

3 The mysterious blonde in the white '56 Ford Thunderbird who starred on *Three's Company*.

_____

4 His role? A fictionalized but still gravelly voiced version of himself eating Popsicles.

_____

5 Five years after playing pensive Curt Henderson, he won a best-actor Oscar for his role in *The Goodbye Girl*.

_____

6 The future *Laverne and Shirley* bottle-capper starred as Steve's high school sweetheart, Laurie.

_____

7 At 12, she played annoying teenybopper Carol. As an actual teen, she starred as Julie Cooper on *One Day at a Time*.

_____

8 She played Peg, making her film debut at the age of 19.

_____

9 For her role as Debbie Dunham, she received a nomination for Academy Award for Best Supporting Actress.

_____

10 The yellow 1932 Ford Coupe defined him as the character John Milner.

_____

Spot the Differences

do you KNOW?

The Uffizi Gallery is in which city?

_____

trivia

- Who was born Stevland Hardaway Judkins?

_____

Slogans 1

ACROSS

1 Framed Disney collectibles
5 Pepsi inventor Bradham
10 Do aquatinting
14 Windward's opposite
15 South American animal
16 Gang of Four's En-Lai
17 Google motto
19 Merry melody
20 Nanny for a night
21 Wages
23 Placed parquetry
25 Slight cut
26 Ologies
30 Bothers
33 Like, on a menu
34 "Winter Song" singer McLachlan
36 "Boggle" need
37 Irish stew meat
39 By and by
41 Circumspection
42 Field marshal Rommel
44 British radials
46 Canard
47 *Das Lied von der Erde* composer
49 Brought to memory
51 Back street
53 Ward in *CSI: NY*
54 Caribbean islands
57 Veldt antelope
61 Scott of *Happy Days*
62 3M motto
64 Extended family
65 Hackneyed
66 Valhalla VIP
67 Broodmares
68 Horrible comics character
69 Door glass

DOWN

1 Scoundrels
2 Morlock victims
3 Time before Easter
4 Pay up, as a bill
5 Type of error
6 Tankard fill
7 Johns
8 Utters
9 Hay job
10 Varied and selective
11 Volkswagen motto
12 Chilly
13 Grass houses
18 Hits with a pitch
22 Cubist Mondrian
24 Get rid of rodents
26 *The Crucible* setting
27 David Copperfield's mother
28 Reebok motto
29 Lustful deity
31 High nest
32 Chased up a trunk
35 "___ to your health!"
38 Ginormous number
40 Andrew Luck target
43 1994 Jodie Foster film
45 Hayek in *Lonely Hearts*
48 Enjoy with gusto
50 Device often used in cafés
52 Yiddish busybody
54 "Alphabet Song" start
55 *The Lion King* heroine
56 Glitch
58 Disney musical
59 Chop cut
60 Rice or Tyler
63 ABBA drummer Brunkert

Concentration—To a T

Determine how to separate the T-figure along the grid lines into three identical pieces.

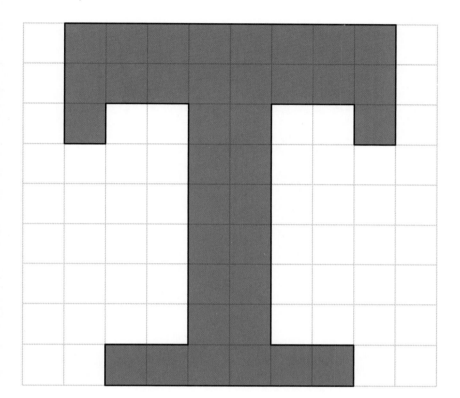

WORD WALL

Beginning at the left side of the wall, make a word by adding one group of letters from each column as you move left to right. When you have found the first word, go back to the second column and start the next word, gathering one group of letters from each column and so on until all the letters are used to make six words.

Sudoku Twin

Fill in the grid so that each row, each column, and each 3 x 3 frame contains every number from 1 to 9. A sudoku twin is two connected 9 x 9 sudokus.

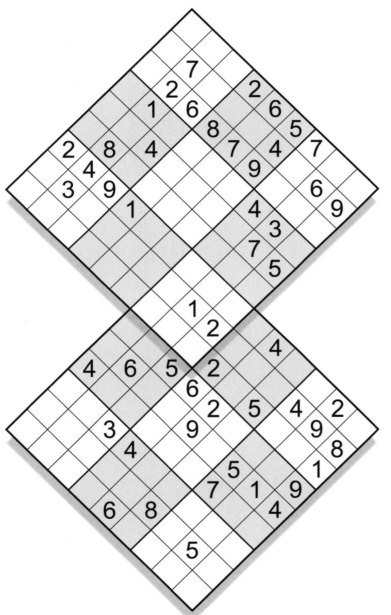

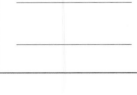

CROSSWORD Big Bands

ACROSS

1 "King of Swing" Benny _____
5 He formed his own Big Band in 1940, Lionel _____
9 Jazz's "Duke"
10 Jazz's "Count"
11 Requisite
13 "The Big Easy," 2 words
16 Actress and director Lupino
17 Tennessee's state flower
19 Peach state (abbr.)
21 Famous 1940s jazz drummer Gene
26 Its logo is a dog listening to a phonograph
28 Los Angeles player
30 Parade motion
33 Watson of the PGA
34 Theater seat categories
35 "The Greatest"
36 Not seniors (abbr.)
37 Slogan: "Put a _____ in your tank"
38 1970s Out of the Blue band (abbr.)
39 Sound system, briefly
40 ER personnel (abbr.)
41 The "Sentimental Gentleman of Swing" (pictured), 2 words
45 Farm cackler
47 Fencing weapon
48 Broadcasting
49 _____meal
50 Type of Big Band music
51 Jack Nicklaus landed most of his drives here

DOWN

1 He led the Army Air Force Band in WWII, 2 words
2 Comedy duo Stan and _____
3 Jazz great Thelonious
4 It comes before Dame
5 Sweetie
6 Normand of silent films
7 Opera that premiered in 1900
8 Christmas carols
12 A beginning for connect
13 Broken-down horse
14 "Tie a Yellow Ribbon 'round the Ole _____ Tree"
15 Mediumlike sensitivity (abbr.)
18 Sign, as a contract
20 "Hello, Dolly!" was a hit for this Louis
22 Boombox button
23 His band was the Gramercy Five, 2 words
24 Satirize
25 Singer who starred in Going My Way
27 Prefix to operative and pilot
29 Make a mistake
31 Syncopated music
32 Bandleader who was married to Betty Grable, with 36 down
36 See 32 down
39 Music genre
41 1979 Bo Derek movie
42 Cat's cry
43 Recorded the first no-hitter in Astros history, _____ Nottebart
44 Big Band _____
46 Airport abbr.
49 This _____ that

Smacker

Which two pairs of lips (1–8) do not belong – knowing that the young lady only had four lipsticks of different colors?

LETTERBLOCKS

Move the letterblocks around so that words associated with the Internet are formed on the top and bottom rows. In some blocks, the letter from the top row has been switched with the letter from the bottom row.

Anagram Mountain

Take a word, mix it up a bit, and what you have is an anagram. Here, by way of a warm-up, are some single-word anagrams. Start at the top and try to find your way down.

LEVEL 1

TVA

TEXN

PRYAT

DUESOX

_____

_____

_____

_____

LEVEL 2

BILEQUO

IDLEARCH

TOMCRUSE

BESKEETAF

_____

_____

_____

_____

LEVEL 3

IUSEVICTORY

DEHORNNODROD

IMBORINGRANTS

ARICHBOGUTOPIA

_____

_____

_____

_____

Slogans 2

ACROSS

1 Drug cop
5 Awestruck, maybe
10 Kindergarten studies
14 Buck's tail
15 Hunter of the PGA
16 ___ *Fiction* (1994)
17 "The Happiest Place on Earth"
19 Fulda feeder
20 Rhône tributary
21 Threshold
23 Secondhand
25 Peppermint Patty's friend
26 Nora Ephron's sister
28 Junk rooms
31 Famed horror-flick street
34 Mountain chain
36 Bridal path
37 Chinese takeout freebie
39 *The Cat in the Hat* author
41 Apprehension
42 To a great extent
44 Fogs up
46 Heredity factor
47 Creates ravines
49 Walks like a tosspot
51 Point out
53 Microscopic
57 Kazoo's cousin
59 Gone from the bowl
60 Pasta ___ Bolognese
61 "Have It Your Way"
65 Foxx in "Sanford and Son"
66 Sporty scarf
67 "So what ___ is new?"
68 Passable
69 Demise
70 Blind a falcon

DOWN

1 Zenith's opposite
2 Come to light
3 Valentine's Day gifts
4 *Victory* author
5 *Little Women* sister
6 Country lass
7 "Told you!"
8 Symbol of China
9 *Bewitched* matriarch
10 Sherry, often
11 "The King of Beers"
12 DuVall in *The Faculty*
13 Full of pep
18 Wriggler wrangler
22 Twice tetra
24 Certain Ivy Leaguers
25 Tobey in *Brothers*
27 Aforementioned
29 Fraternity
30 It will be, to Quixote
31 Kathryn of *Law and Order: Criminal Intent*
32 One who speaks with forked tongue
33 "I'm Lovin' It"
35 Latin 101 verb
38 Mayan city of gold
40 Banana stalk
43 Himalayan mystery
45 Less forthright
48 *Arabian Nights* sailor
50 ___ *on a Plane* (2006)
52 Bring about
54 Functional
55 Keyed-up
56 Cologne cherub
57 They can make waves
58 Geppetto's goldfish
62 Elvis Presley's label
63 *You've ___ Mail* (1998)
64 Ordinal suffix

BRAIN FITNESS Stop-and-Go Anagrams

The groups of eight letters in each of these lights can form anagrams. In the easy (green) lights, your challenge is to find one eight-letter anagram that can be formed with those letters. In the medium (amber) lights, you have to find two different eight-letter words, and in the difficult (red) lights there are three eight-letter words to find — and maybe more! Each letter in each light is used only once.

LEVEL 3

LEVEL 2

LEVEL 1

trivia

• What are the names of King Lear's daughters?

The Well-Read Reader

Just jump right in and see how well you've been staying abreast of the literary landscape.

1. Who was born July 31, 1965, and grew up to write one of the most popular series of children's books of all time?

   a. Cornelia Funke
   b. Christopher Paolini
   c. J. K. Rowling

2. Whose collection forms the cornerstone of the book collection housed at the Bibliothèque Nationale de France?

   a. Jean Paul Sartre
   b. Victor Hugo
   c. Charles V

3. Around 1450 Johannes Gutenberg invented a press that used movable metal type, but what country to the east had been producing books using carved woodblocks as early as the seventh century?

   a. Japan
   b. China
   c. Korea

4. Which book has sold more than 40 million copies since 1930?

   a. *Better Homes and Gardens Cook Book*
   b. *Better Homes and Gardens Complete Guide to Quilting*
   c. *Better Homes and Gardens Plants for All Seasons*

5. What was Stephen King's first novel?

   a. *Salem's Lot*
   b. *Carrie*
   c. *The Dark Tower*

6. Who wrote the controversial novel *Satanic Verses* in 1989 and received death threats from Islamic militants?

   a. Ayaan Hirsi Ali
   b. Michael Ondaatje
   c. Salman Rushdie

7. What do J. D. Salinger's *The Catcher in the Rye*, Harper Lee's *To Kill a Mockingbird*, John Steinbeck's *Of Mice and Men*, and Mark Twain's *The Adventures of Huckleberry Finn* have in common?

   a. They all won the Pulitzer Prize.
   b. They've all been used to challenge the First Amendment.
   c. They've all been nominated for a National Book Award.

8. Who wrote *Nickel and Dimed: On (Not) Getting By in America*?

   a. Barbara Ehrenreich
   b. Barbara Kingsolver
   c. Michael Pollen

9. Who wrote *Mr. Peabody's Apples*?

   a. Katie Couric
   b. Jerry Seinfeld
   c. Madonna

10. In 1906, what industry did Upton Sinclair expose as a public-health threat in his landmark work, *The Jungle*?

    a. Meatpacking
    b. Textiles
    c. Sugar

BRAINSNACK® Flag It Up

How should you order the signal flags FZG so that they are a logical continuation of the series QIT? Pay attention to the arrows.

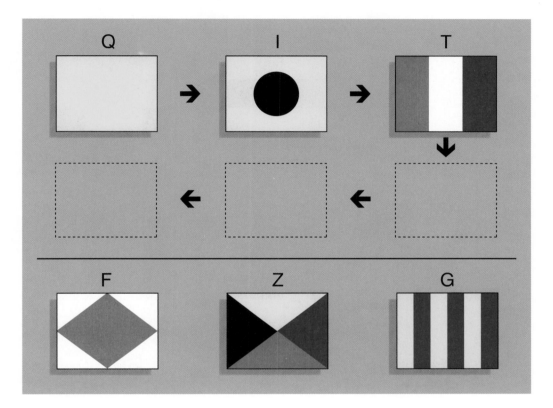

M*A*S*H

ACROSS

1 She played "Hot Lips," 2 words
8 Mountain in *The Sound of Music*
10 Sushi order
11 Command, for short
12 Cub opponent
13 First word of the *M*A*S*H* theme song
16 Tarzan extra
18 Golden State (abbr.)
19 Italian actress Sophia
20 Capt. Benjamin Pierce's nickname
24 Reverberate
26 Two-way prefix
27 *Where _____ Dare* (1968), Clint Eastwood and Richard Burton movie
29 Taking another country by force
33 Louisville Slugger wood
34 Start of three John Wayne movie titles
35 Margaret "Hot Lips" _____
37 Location indicator
39 Yogi in baseball
40 Ostrich relative
41 Chocolate snack rolls
43 Unit of electricity
44 Fairytale creature
46 Capt. John McIntyre's nickname
48 Doll
49 Pontiac Grand _____
50 Honky-tonk country singer Joe
51 Hockey legend Orr
52 *M*A*S*H* star first name

DOWN

1 McLean Stevenson played him, 4 words (rank abbr.)
2 Walter _____ O'Reilly
3 *Billy Budd* (1962) star _____ Stamp
4 Starting point for Arnold Palmer
5 *M*A*S*H* star last name
6 Past tense of "is"
7 Three-time prefix
8 Dennis the Menace's mom
9 Pumpkin, for example
14 Land of the free (abbr.)
15 Movie star Doris _____
17 Emma of *The Avengers*
20 *M*A*S*H* character B.J. _____
21 Org. for heavyweights
22 The Cincinnati _____
23 Corp. Klinger was always angling for a Section _____
25 Common school abbreviation
28 Sam Cooke didn't know much about it in "Wonderful World"
30 Des Moines' state (abbr.)
31 Code-cracking org.
32 Cool Hand _____
(1967), Paul Newman movie
35 "Thank _____ for Little Girls," Maurice Chevalier song
36 1960s guru's religious community
38 "_____ of Love" (No. 1 hit in 1964)
42 Toxic manmade chemical agent
45 Toy company _____ Schwarz
47 Father of Soul _____ Charles

Sudoku X

Fill in the grid so that each row, each column, and each 3 x 3 frame contains every number from 1 to 9. The two main diagonals of the grid also contain every number from 1 to 9.

			8				9	
		8		7				
						5		
1			3			2		
9	4				5			
3								
		1		6				3
				9		7	5	
		7	1	5	4			

do you KNOW

What is pteridology the study of?

BLOCK ANAGRAM

Form the word that is described in the parentheses using the letters above the grid. Extra letters are already in the right place.

SCARELESS (2012 Olympic gold medal women's middle weight boxing [75kg])

	L			S		A		H	I		D	

Binairo

Complete the grid with zeros and ones until there are 6 zeros and 6 ones in every row and every column. No more than two of the same number can be next to or under each other. Rows or columns with exactly the same content are not allowed. There is only one valid solution.

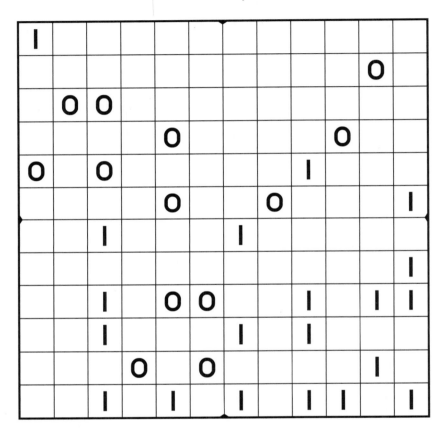

do you KNOW

What did Howard Carter discover in 1922?

Blooms

Which flower branch (1–6) does not belong?

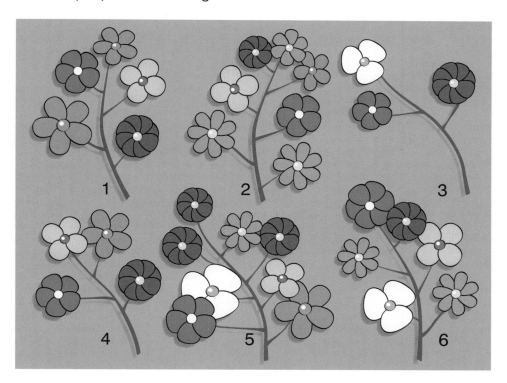

QUICK CROSSWORD

Place the words listed below in the crossword grid.

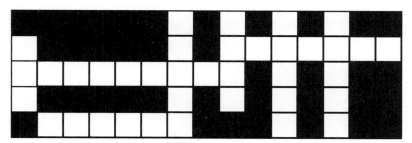

IMPULSE ANIMATION LIVING MAN BEING FLESH SPARK ZING

Hairstyles

ACROSS

1 Like good cheese or wine
5 Gas used in flashes and lamps
10 Cravings
14 Moth stage
15 Wide in surprise
16 Boxing Day tsunami locale, Banda _____
17 2017 U.S. Open site, _____ Hills
18 Sound
19 Punjab, India, district
20 1950s slicked-back hairstyle
22 Casino employee
24 Commercials
25 1960s conical hairstyle
26 Timeless short hairstyle (2 wds.)
30 Ferber, who wrote Show Boat and Giant
31 Ness of The Untouchables
32 Singer Perry
33 Football field lengths (abbr.)
36 The A in A.D.
37 Large horned mammal
39 Slender
40 _____ and cheese
41 Enlist again
42 "_____ shining sea" (2 wds.)
43 1948 Hitchcock movie
44 1970s layered hairstyle (2 wds.)
46 Haircut named for a medieval servant
49 Type of sleep
50 After home or letter
51 Fairy hairdo popular in the 1960s (2 wds.)
56 Exceeded the limit
57 Beige
59 Modeled
60 Ultimatum word

61 Mistake
62 Character in Disney's *Frozen*
63 Bambi, for example
64 Lake flora
65 Stitched area

DOWN

1 Imitated
2 Religious leader or expert
3 Long poem
4 Cool and wet
5 Idyllic place
6 Self-centered person
7 Goes with hammer
8 Military short form
9 Required (2 wds.)

10 Maker of motorcycles and keyboards
11 Bad bacteria
12 Israeli desert
13 Offer a piece
21 Diplomacy
23 _____ meeny miny moe
25 Kidney or butter
26 Gymnast's balance _____
27 Arm bone
28 30th element
29 Spot for 37 Across
32 1978-'79 Tigers pitcher Young
33 Slangy agreement
34 Info
35 Kiss, in England

37 Lois Lane's job
38 _____, Dewey and Louie
39 _____ Paul guitar
41 Housecoat
42 Freight truck
43 Process fat
44 Camera stand
45 Witches
46 Arranged
47 Fruit
48 They're in flocks
51 Unblemished
52 Rams' mates
53 _____ Haan shoes
54 _____ Major or Minor
55 Cardinals or Blue Jays, for example
58 Plural of is

WORD SEARCH Cocktails

All the words are hidden vertically, horizontally, or diagonally—in both directions. The letters that remain unused form a sentence from left to right.

```
B E B L A C K W I D O W U R N
I S R N G C O A C A K H T A T
I O A L A H N I R I P I A C H
S R Z C O N T K A Q I S O N G
A L I S M A L I L U Q K T U I
A E L N T W I K T I Y Y I P N
G M I O F H H I N R I S J I S
S I A K I R R I A I G O O N S
N M N M H R L P T E R U M K E
I A S F E C I I T E E R N L L
L R U T I R A S A G L E A A D
L G N M L Z I C H N O A H D N
O A R A O R Z C N C Y L D Y E
C R I I T O H A A T O T I Y S
M I S T L B I T M N B F S E F
O T E A O R R E B E O I F U N
T A G I S O L A D Y L O V E R
E R V E D Y C U B A L I B R E
```

- AMERICANO
- BLACK WIDOW
- BRAZILIAN SUNRISE
- CAIPIRINHA
- CUBA LIBRE
- DAIQUIRI
- ENDLESS NIGHT
- GIN FIZZ
- IRISH COFFEE
- KIRR
- LADY LOVER
- MAI TAI
- MANHATTAN
- MARGARITA
- MELROSE
- MOJITO
- PINK LADY
- ROB ROY
- RUSTY NAIL
- TOM COLLINS
- WAIKIKI
- WHISKY SOUR
- WHITE LADY

Movie Drunks

ACROSS

1 Catty remark
5 Runner-up
10 Mideast capital
14 Not aweather
15 Prefix meaning "within"
16 Claudius I's successor
17 He acted drunk in *Independence Day*
19 Narrow the gap
20 Difficult
21 Muffle
23 Early fifth-century date
24 Cool-headed
25 Clothing, in slang
29 Exude
32 "Hit the ___ Jack": Charles
33 Thread reel
35 Steep rugged rock
36 No special one
37 Capek robot play
38 Nadal's aunt
39 Unconscious state
41 Chewable leaf
43 Fruit's coat
44 Kris ___
46 Instants
48 Stead
49 Small inlet
50 Fortify
53 Isolate
57 Insect wings
58 He acted drunk in *Days of Wine and Roses*
60 Russo of *Buddy*
61 *Misery* psycho
62 *About ___* (Hugh Grant film)
63 Rocker Rundgren
64 *Truth of Touch* musician
65 Aunt Bee's sister

DOWN

1 Prefix for normal
2 Suffix for gland
3 Tear asunder
4 Sign at a sale
5 Dehydration remedy
6 Unpleasant task
7 NYC's Penn ___: Abbr.
8 Ill-tempered goddess
9 Zealot
10 Heavenly
11 He acted drunk in *Rio Bravo*
12 Dr. Foreman of *House*
13 Second to ___
18 *Star Wars* Jedi master
22 Youngster
25 Overdubbing unit
26 Good name
27 He acted drunk in *The Lost Weekend*
28 Shopping binge
29 *Santa Fe Songs* composer
30 Trace of disgrace
31 "My goodness!"
34 Not in
40 Pizzelle flavoring
41 Colorful crested bird
42 "Diamonds Are a Girl's Best Friend" singer
43 Macho guy
45 "Scram!"
47 Elephant's fear
50 Simpson or Starr
51 Butter alternative
52 Frog genus
53 Rind
54 Shield boss
55 Portal
56 "Storms in Africa" singer
59 Wolf Blitzer's network

BRAINSNACK® **Greener Grass**

Which zone (1–7) on the map should be colored green?

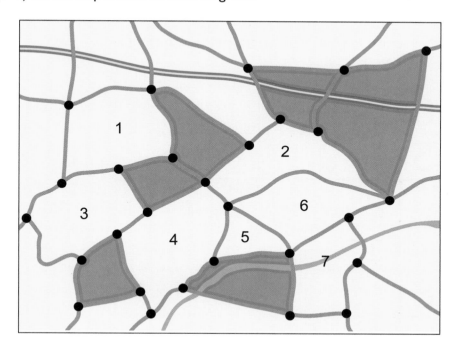

QUICK WORD SEARCH

Find the herbs and spices listed below in the word search grid.

C	U	M	I	N	U	T	M	E	G	L	E	D	U	M
B	A	L	H	A	M	C	A	S	S	I	A	R	E	V
U	U	Y	R	O	V	A	S	C	I	L	R	A	G	B
E	E	F	F	O	C	L	O	V	E	R	E	P	A	C
W	K	G	W	O	R	R	A	Y	C	H	I	V	E	S

**CAPER CASSIA CHIVES CLOVER COFFEE CUMIN GARLIC LEDUM
MAHLAB NUTMEG SAVORY YARROW**

Sudoku

Fill in the grid so that each row, each column, and each 3 x 3 frame contains every number from 1 to 9.

			6	8				
		6	8					
		5		9			3	
5			2			6	7	
		1			3			
	6	8						1
	4				7		9	
	9				5			
7			9	3	1		8	

triVia
- Who married Oona O'Neill in 1943?

SYMBOL SUMS

Can you work out these number sums using three of these four symbols? $+ - \div \times$

$$24 \square 4 \square 6 \square 4 = 42$$

174

Sport Maze

Draw the shortest way from the ball to the goal. You can only move along vertical and horizontal lines, not along diagonal lines. The figure on each square indicates the number of squares the ball must be moved in the same direction. You can change direction at each stop.

3	3	4	5	4	2
3	1	3	3	4	5
5	1	2	3	4	1
1	4	3	3	4	2
3	1	3	2	3	3
●	2	2	5	2	2

do you KNOW?

What did Walter Frederick Morrison invent?

ONE LETTER LESS OR MORE

The word on the right side contains the letters of the word on the left side, plus or minus the letter in the middle. One letter is already in the right place.

O U T S K I R T +E ☐ ☐ ☐ ☐ I ☐ ☐ ☐ ☐

Word Sudoku

Complete the grid so that each row, each column, and each 3 x 3 frame contains the nine letters from the black box below. The hidden nine-letter word is in the diagonal from top left to bottom right.

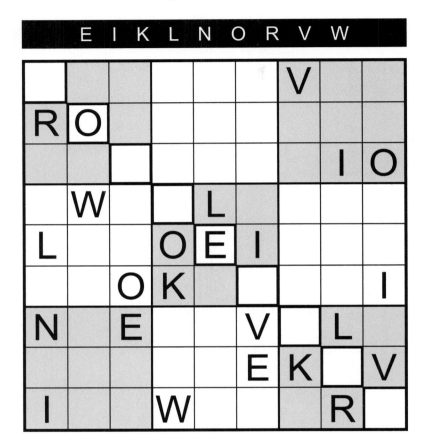

E I K L N O R V W

E I K L N O R V W

trivia

- Whose pseudonym is Richard Bachman?

_____

CROSSWORD Song Tributes

ACROSS

1 Cantina cooker
5 Gandhi, e.g.
10 "___ lively!"
14 Rock stratum
15 Garnish
16 Bridgestone product
17 Grateful Dead song about an engineer
19 André's girlfriend
20 Chevy van
21 Speech defect
23 Concedes
26 Kind of boom
27 *Li'l Abner* cartoonist
28 Sounded like sonar
31 Cobra genus
34 Inflatable floatables
37 Five-star Las Vegas hotel
38 Bygone Turkish title
39 Boxing org.
40 Fortify
41 Iditarod Trail end
43 Long-billed bird
45 "Just ___ bit more"
46 Order of the day
48 Equivalent
50 Bowls over
52 Let back in
56 Book supplement
58 Bane of banks
59 Ballpark beverage
60 Weezer song about a rock pioneer
64 Dragonfly wings
65 Royo in *Red Tails*
66 Bit of information
67 Act the caretaker
68 McFadden of *Star Trek: TNG*
69 See socially

DOWN

1 Award for Colin Firth
2 It may have a "no pets" clause
3 Keeps going
4 "Made in ___": Toby Keith
5 Pilgrimage to Mecca
6 "What'll ___?": Berlin
7 *Sine qua* ___
8 Donna Karan creation
9 Pulls the plug on
10 It's needed to finish a marathon
11 Taylor Swift song about a singer
12 Huron's neighbor
13 Jury candidate
18 Exercise discipline
22 Singer DiFranco
24 *Car Talk* network
25 Salmon eggs
29 Hibernia
30 Maggie Smith's title
31 Zola novel
32 Awestruck
33 Eagles song about a film actor
35 Fox Mulder's employer
36 Slender candle
42 Became a member
43 Ballast unit
44 Garden snake's prey?
45 Smartphone platform
47 Horse hue
49 To ___ his own
51 Finnish bath
53 Sicily's neighbor
54 Speck in the sea
55 Aromatic herb
56 Like ___ out of hell
57 Proofer's mark
61 *Silent Spring* killer
62 Dr. of rap
63 "By all means!"

Themeless 4

ACROSS

1. Some are set to music
6. Financial channel
10. Boston cager, for short
14. *Gosford Park* maid
15. "Deck the Halls" syllables
16. Moonfish
17. Seaboard
18. Daggoo's captain
19. Kudrow in *Analyze This*
20. 1992 skating gold medalist
23. Org. for dockworkers
24. "Losing My Religion" band
25. *War Horse* director
34. Heraldic bearing
35. Mere
36. Rara avis
37. "Sorry, lassie!"
38. Summer hours in NY
39. Blood-group system
40. "Send in the Clowns" starter
42. "Lady ___": Chris de Burgh
44. Iowa State University city
45. Traits
48. Be light, at poker
49. Got comfy
50. *Harry Potter and the Deathly Hallows* star
59. *Phantom of the Opera*
60. Cream-of-the-crop
61. Asian wild sheep
62. Sicilian peak
63. Tot's grandmother
64. Prefix with fluoride
65. Does some batiking
66. Harriet Beecher Stowe book
67. Collectible Ford model

DOWN

1. Gregory in *The Omen*
2. Swan genus
3. Morales of *Caprica*
4. Communiqué
5. Colonize
6. French Open court surface
7. Okinawa city
8. "Kapow!"
9. Musical set in Berlin
10. Peter Falk role
11. Big production
12. Eyewinker
13. Chiang Mai cuisine
21. Olympians Crocker and Thorpe
22. Salon goo
25. Chevy subcompact
26. It's not recycled
27. Makarova of tennis
28. Hound's clue
29. San Diego player
30. Bury
31. As a friend, in Paris
32. Medieval violin
33. Yucky
41. Siberian sleighs
42. Greenland's neighbor
43. Harrow blade
44. Dressed
46. Reverential wonder
47. Greet a major
50. Quitclaim
51. Like Montmartre
52. Lowest card in pinochle
53. Sound of the surf
54. "Snowbird" singer Murray
55. Numbed up
56. ___ and starts
57. Price of a ride
58. Carrier to Jerusalem

Keep Going

Start on a blank square of your choice and connect as many blank squares as possible with one single continuous line. You can only connect squares along vertical and horizontal lines, not along diagonal lines. You must continue the connecting lineup until the next obstacle, i.e., the border of the box, a black square, or a square that has already been used. You can change direction at any obstacle you meet. Each square can only be used once. The number of blank squares that will be left unused is marked in the upper square. There is more than one solution. We only show one solution.

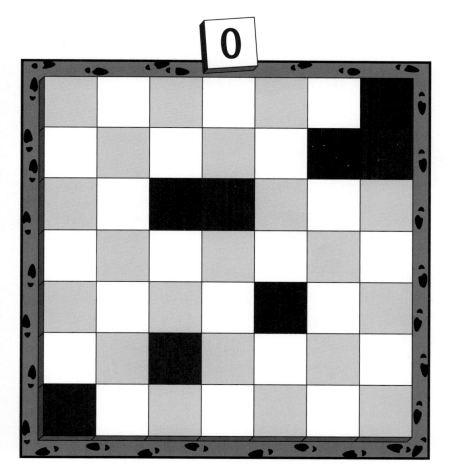

0

do you KNOW?

What did John Stith Pemberton invent on May 8, 1886, in Atlanta Georgia?

Number Crunch

Numberlock puzzles look like a crossword but uses numbers instead. Fit the numbers listed into the grid. One number has been inserted in the correct position to get you started.

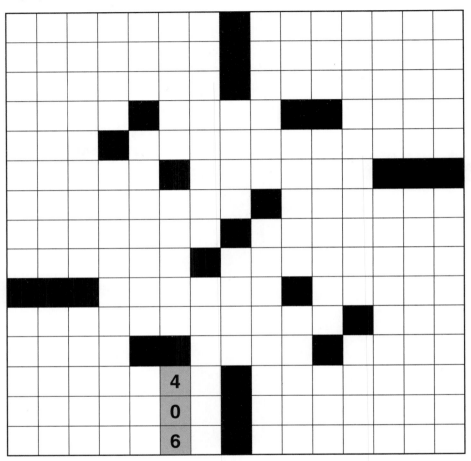

3 digits	7 digits
107	1027170
163	2068157
236	2346453
247	4003765
406	5431747
548	5438302
601	5724625
633	6255140
	6271488
4 digits	6739368
1036	6815828
2810	8017348
3659	8474316
4475	9173528
7324	9269582
9216	9617006
9404	
9529	8 digits
9788	45102846
9879	75016014
	83827248
5 digits	85007825
13540	
25294	9 digits
27896	138831523
48260	564314872
55004	741769179
57357	811500450
70253	926928469
72694	930264313
81997	
84628	10 digits
88237	9019160573
91510	9199076460
6 digits	11 digits
123830	54703110786
239307	74965712050
526985	
814065	
939962	
956639	

trivia

• Who played Gandhi in the 1982 film?

_____

TRIVIA QUIZ **Bach to the Classics**

Dig deep into your fund of musical knowledge to find the answers to the questions below.

1. Which of the following was composed by Aram Khachaturian?
   a. "Foil Dance"
   b. "Sabre Dance"
   c. "Epee Dance"

2. Who was known as "The Waltz King"?
   a. Johann Strauss
   b. Laurence Welk
   c. John Phillip Sousa

3. What year provides the title for the overture by Tchaikovsky to commemorate the defeat of Napoleon?
   a. 1814
   b. 1812
   c. 1776

4. What does the musical term "forte" mean?
   a. Loud
   b. Soft
   c. Do your best

5. Which symphony by Beethoven was used in the Second World War because its opening four notes are similar to the Morse code for V?
   a. Symphony No. 3
   b. Symphony No. 9
   c. Symphony No. 5

6. Where was Mozart born?
   a. Vienna
   b. Salzburg
   c. Strasburg

7. Which musical instrument is Stradivarius NOT known for making?
   a. Clarinet
   b. Violin
   c. Cello

8. What is the highest singing female voice?
   a. Soprano
   b. Tenor
   b. Alto

9. Which orchestra is sometimes referred to by the initials NYPO?
   a. Neil Young's Polytechnic Orchestra
   b. New York Philharmonic Orchestra
   c. New York Pops Orchestra

10. What name is given to the principal female singer in an opera?
    a. Carlotta
    b. Diva
    c. Prima donna

trivia
• Who composed the opera Peter Grimes?

Hidden Theme

ACROSS

1 Monica of tennis
6 Synth pioneer Robert
10 Fourth person
14 Suffix for fraud
15 French coin
16 "___ creature was stirring ..."
17 2011 Selena Gomez film
19 Calvary initials
20 Knotted up
21 Emmy winner for *Roots*
23 Pipe elbow
24 Memo
25 Routes to the Supreme Court
29 Cherished
32 Pâté de foie ___
33 Hidden title related to clue answers
35 The Aswan dams it
36 Ray Charles hit "Hide ___ Hair"
37 Guitar bars
38 Jeremy of the NBA
39 Horned buglers
41 "___ Cookie Blues": Lonnie Mack
42 Much of the time
43 Targets of a pat-down
45 Jim Henson creations
48 Country singer Gosdin
49 Drink daintily
50 Put up a monument
53 Sense of unease
57 Painter Guido
58 Golden State
60 Spectrum color
61 Pre-Soviet ruler
62 Spills the beans
63 Spud buds
64 Wynken's boat
65 Satisfy a thirst

DOWN

1 Abacus results
2 North Carolina college
3 Siberian river
4 Daily specials
5 Adler who taught Brando
6 Hoover Dam's lake
7 "___ Day Will Come"
8 Heraldic wreath
9 "Oh dear!"
10 Jennifer in *Office Space*
11 Utah's ___ Salt Flats
12 To be, to Henri
13 Dragon's den
18 Convent room
22 *The Huffington Post* parent
25 Chloë of Celtic Woman
26 Laborer
27 MetLife Building's NYC locale
28 Battle mementos
29 Quidditch transport
30 *Adam Bede* novelist
31 Fender flaws
34 Jungle swinger
37 Makes a nexus
40 *Homo sapiens*, for one
42 Garb
44 Doggy bag item
46 F-16 wing letters
47 Frequent fliers
50 Kathryn of *Law & Order: Criminal Intent*
51 Bank, in a way
52 Short race
53 Swampland
54 *Lost ___ Mancha* (2002)
55 Tie fabric
56 Lessen the load
59 Mekong River dweller

Sudoku Twin

Fill in the grid so that each row, each column, and each 3 x 3 frame contains every number from 1 to 9. A sudoku twin is two connected 9 x 9 sudokus.

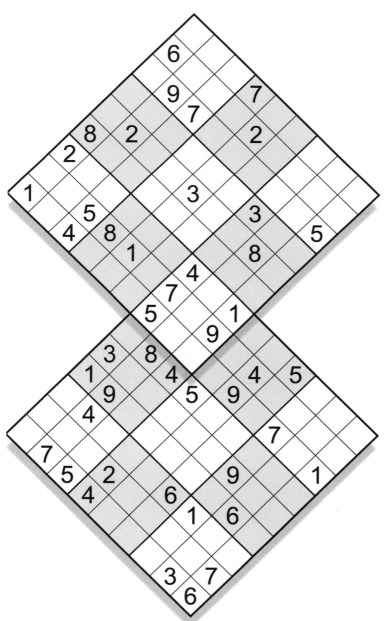

delete ONE

Delete one letter from

DRAMAS SAW DECAY

and rearrange the rest to find which ones won't get these.

_____

_____

Sunny

Where will the sun shine? With the knowledge that each arrow points to a place where a symbol should be, can you locate the sunny spots? The symbols cannot be next to each other vertically, horizontally, or diagonally. A symbol cannot be placed on top of an arrow. We show one symbol.

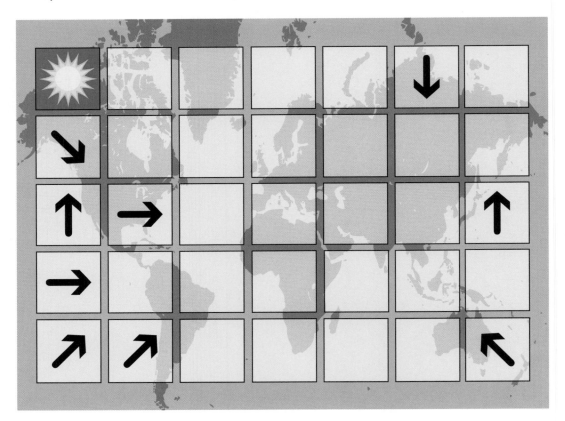

TRIANAGRAM

Three-word groups of anagrams are also called triplets or trianagrams.
Complete the group:

LEASH _ _ _ _ _   _ _ _ _ _

CROSSWORD Holiday Carols

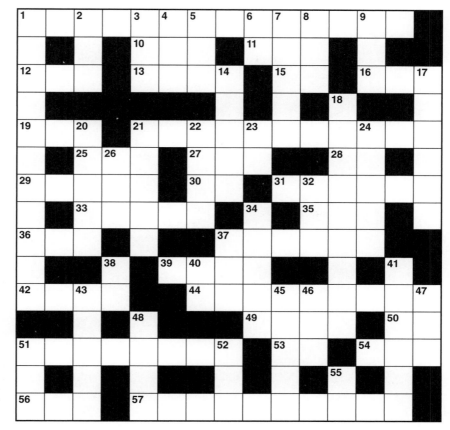

ACROSS

1 Carol that ends with the line, "Your boughs can teach a lesson," 3 words
10 Scottish refusal
11 Dove call
12 Psalm 23: "My _____ runneth over"
13 Popular Christmas carol, 4 words, goes with 18 down
15 Havre preceder
16 Creeping plant featured in a popular Christmas carol
19 Genesis 1: "So God created _____ in his own image…"
21 One of the singers in a popular carol
25 Wedding vow, 2 words
27 "We three kings of Orient _____"
28 "I understand"
29 Gabriel, for one
30 Manuscript, for short
31 Wide-sleeved robe
33 They're decked with boughs of holly
35 Many words in the carol in 33 across
36 Started a fire
37 Very peaceful Christmas carol, goes with 20 down
39 Cake decorator
42 Wise men came from the _____
44 "Little town" in a Christmas carol
49 Listen
50 Pie a _____ mode
51 See 1 down
53 Compass point
54 Subject of many seasonal wishes and part of a popular carol title
56 Past tense of "is"
57 He was "little" in a Christmas carol, 2 words

DOWN

1 Popular carol, 5 words, goes with 51 across (variation)
2 Jump
3 _____ hurry, 2 words
4 Watched
5 Oolong, for one
6 DC alternative
7 Ashford and Simpson's "_____ as a Rock"
8 Low digit
9 Biblical judge and priest
14 They're always advancing
17 Ribbon tied round an old oak tree, in song
18 Goes with 13 across
20 See 37 across
21 Tree that is featured in a popular Christmas carol
22 Male sheep
23 _____ Monde (French daily)
24 Casper, the Friendly _____
26 Federal contraband agency (abbr.)
32 French island
34 Christmas celebrates Jesus' _____
37 Observe
38 Sinai, for example (abbr.)
40 Radio type
41 Tune
43 Three came sailing in, in a Christmas carol
45 Therefore
46 Attorney's expertise
47 Memorial Day month
48 Place for tools
51 Matthew 22: "Many are called, but _____ are chosen"
52 On the _____ (as a fugitive)
55 Weight measurement (abbr.)

Rack 'Em

Place the billiard balls on the circles with the corresponding color so that the sum in all columns, rows, and the two diagonals is 49.

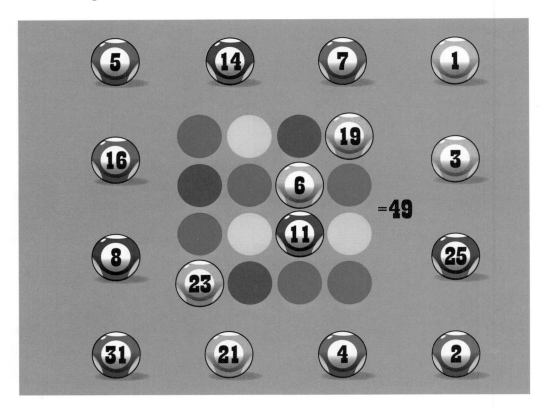

=49

DOUBLETALK

Homophones are words that share the same pronunciation, no matter how they are spelled. If they are spelled differently, then they are called heterographs. Find heterographs meaning:

A FEW and ADDITION

Binairo

Complete the grid with zeros and ones until there are 5 zeros and 6 ones in every row and every column. No more than two of the same number can be next to or under each other. Rows or columns with exactly the same content are not allowed. There is only one valid solution.

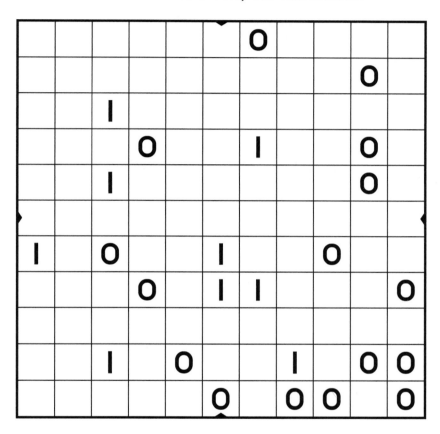

do you KNOW?

In Greek mythology, what creature did Theseus slay in the labyrinth?

_____

TRIANAGRAM

Three-word groups of anagrams are also called triplets or trianagrams.
Complete the group:

LAMENESS   _ _ _ _ _ _ _ _   _ _ _ _ _ _ _ _

Namesakes 1

ACROSS

1 Max Ernst's movement
5 Quite full
10 "___ brillig ...": Carroll
14 CB sign-off
15 He defeated Lee at Gettysburg
16 Put on
17 Cain/Short namesake?
19 *Say Anything ...* actress Skye
20 Trial
21 Went to an event
23 Historic Normandy city
25 Panky's partner
26 Gunslinger wear
30 Spring flowers
33 Egg cells
34 City NNE of Cologne
36 City in northern India
37 Smart-alecky
39 Pulled
41 Speak drunkenly
42 Flynn with dashing roles
44 Less dated
46 French season
47 Fashions
49 Gave notice
51 Body-shop concerns
53 Like Wimbledon telecasts
54 Frightening
57 French painter
61 Thomas ___ Edison
62 Rockefeller/Arnold namesake?
64 French-cuff feature
65 1912 Nobelist Root
66 Shrimp removal
67 It may be stemmed or turned
68 Collar inserts
69 Opera singer Haugland

DOWN

1 Flintstones' pet bird
2 Allege as a fact
3 Departed
4 James of *Gunsmoke*
5 Most compact
6 ___ Lingus airline
7 "See ya!"
8 Cabaret singer Piaf
9 Like some canines
10 Scintillates
11 Guthrie/Ginsberg namesake?
12 *Rule, Britannia!* composer
13 Tennis ranking
18 Unglossy finish
22 Sir Geraint's wife
24 Welles in *Chimes at Midnight*
26 Expectations
27 Manifest
28 King/Frost namesake?
29 Seamstress
31 Bobsled track
32 Became a father
35 Staircase post
38 Put up with
40 Craving
43 Capture on film
45 In two
48 Curling rocks
50 League of Nations city
52 Turn iron into steel
54 Observe Yom Kippur
55 Giantess who wrestled Thor
56 Lamb's nom de plume
58 Classical theaters
59 Beatnik's "Got it!"
60 Cub legend Sandberg
63 Lacking

TRIVIA QUIZ **Flying High**

You're sure to make a smooth landing if you can score the right answer
on all of these curious airplane questions.

1. Who piloted the *Spirit of St. Louis*, from Roosevelt Field, New York, to Le Bourget Field outside Paris in 1927 to make the world's first solo nonstop transatlantic flight?

_____

2. Where did Captain Chesley Sullenberger make an emergency landing of US Airways flight 1549 on January 15, 2009?

_____

3. Who was Bessie Coleman?

_____

4. In 2006, what did the U.S. Travel and Security Administration mandate for all carry-on baggage as a security measure?

_____

5. Who was born on July 24, 1897, and was believed to have died in 1937 on a flight between New Guinea and Howland Island?

_____

6. Conceived in 1962, the supersonic Concorde jet was an unlikely collaboration between which two governments?

_____

7. Which city is served by Santa Cruz airport?

_____

8. How many passengers could the early corporate-style jets such as the Lear 23 carry as a full load?

_____

9. What name is given to the design of aircraft with the tail wing in front of the main wing?

_____

10. At the 1973 Paris Air Show, the Soviet version of the Concorde crashed. By what nickname was the plane better known?

_____

11. Britain was the first country to introduce a jet passenger line. What was its name?

_____

12. Apart from being the fastest aircraft when built, what is the other unique claim to fame of the rocket-powered X-15?

_____

13. What 1960s vintage aircraft still holds the record for the fastest operational manned flight?

_____

14. During World War II, how did one join the "caterpillar club"?

_____

Word Sudoku

Complete the grid so that each row, each column, and each 3 x 3 frame contains the nine letters from the black box below. The hidden nine-letter word is in the diagonal from top left to bottom right.

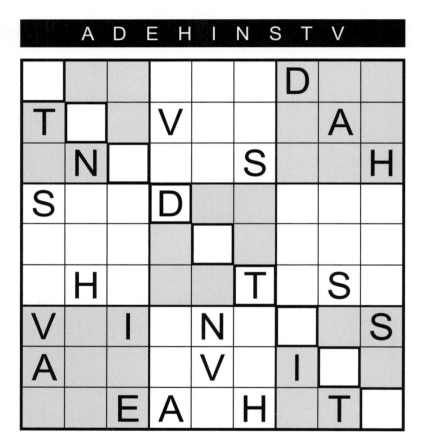

A D E H I N S T V

						D		
T			V				A	
	N				S			H
S		D						
	H			T		S		
V	I		N					S
A			V		I			
		E	A	H		T		

trivia

- What is the name of Olivia de Havilland's sister?

Rearrange the letters of the phrase below to form a cognate anagram, one that is related or connected in meaning to the original phrase. The answer can be one or more words.

O END

CROSSWORD Namesakes 2

ACROSS

1 Jackie in *Rush Hour*
5 ___ pushers (culottes)
10 *Pygmalion* playwright
14 First-class
15 *Moulin ___!* (2001)
16 The Phantom's horse
17 Perry/Sutherland namesake?
19 One of Medusa's sisters
20 Got the lead out
21 Bad poetry
23 The world, to Atlas
25 Obviously sad
26 Links up
30 Blue-pencil
33 Boxing great
34 Reporters' areas
36 Cute marsupial
37 Latvian capital
39 Disrobe
41 Clutch
42 In full view
44 À la King
46 "Ode ___ Grecian Urn"
47 Liquefied
49 Tapered ship flags
51 Takes the bait
53 Bouncer's station
54 Shopkeeper
57 Danes in *Romeo + Juliet*
61 Jewish month
62 Liotta/Grodin namesake?
64 Risotto ingredient
65 The Weasleys' owl
66 "___ I a stinker?": Bugs Bunny
67 Savvy pair?
68 Witherspoon in *Penelope*
69 Art gallery of London

DOWN

1 NASCAR legend Yarborough
2 "The Children's ___": Longfellow
3 "She's a Lady" lyricist
4 Liam in *Battleship*
5 Puts on
6 Many milleniums
7 Pair
8 Brightly burning
9 Bookkeeping book
10 Border collie
11 Fonda/Copland namesake?

12 Gross in *Arthur's Quest*
13 Sheep shearings
18 Huge star in Cygnus
22 Carnival freak
24 Kind of pen?
26 Squash shot
27 Martini ingredient
28 Mansell/Lee namesake?
29 Throat infection
31 Eastwood in *Unforgiven*
32 Ávila appetizers
35 Begat
38 "A" and "an"
40 Game with 48 cards
43 Hebrew T

45 Nancy Springer detective
48 More prized
50 Genesis landfall
52 Pitfall
54 *Jeopardy* creator Griffin
55 *Night* author Wiesel
56 City in Lebanon
58 Olympic skater Kulik
59 Budget item
60 Renaissance patron
63 Romaine lettuce

Healthy Appetites

After a strenuous game of soccer, six boys headed out for a snack at a local café. They all sat around a table as shown on the diagram below, but no boy occupied a seat whose identification letter is the same as the first letter of his last name. Being very hungry, the boys ordered six different scones, then followed this with six more scones, so that overall each boy ate two. However, no boy finished with the same type of scone as he started with. Munch your way through the clues below to discover not only the boys' full names and where they sat but which type of scone each boy chose first and second.

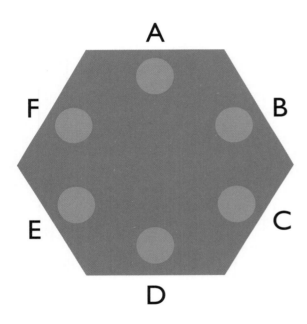

1. The identification letter of the seat occupied by the boy who started with a pineapple scone occurs one place earlier in the alphabet than that occupied by Mr. Potter, who chose to start with a black-currant cake. Mr. Veness occupied seat F.

2. Adam (who didn't have a sugar scone second) sat one place clockwise (from your point of view as you look at the diagram) of the boy who started with a sugar scone and rapidly followed this with a pineapple scone. The boy in seat E started with a banana scone. Fred ordered a lemon scone second.

3 Still looking in a clockwise direction at the plan of the table below, David Symes sat one place clockwise of the boy whose second choice was the sugar scone and who, in turn, sat one place clockwise of Brian. The boy who chose the blueberry scone second does not have the last name Lowe.

4 Ewan occupied seat B. Fred isn't Mr. Willard. The boy in seat D, who started with a strawberry scone, doesn't have the last name Robertson or Willard.

	FIRST NAMES						LAST NAMES						FIRST SCONE						SECOND SCONE					
	Adam	Brian	David	Ewan	Fred	Graham	Lowe	Potter	Roberston	Symes	Veness	Willard	Banana	Black-currant	Blueberry	Pineapple	Strawberry	Sugar	Banana	Blueberry	Lemon	Pineapple	Strawberry	Sugar
SEAT Seat A																								
Seat B																								
Seat C																								
Seat D																								
Seat E																								
Seat F																								
SECOND SCONE Banana second																			
Blueberry second																			
Lemon second																			
Pineapple second																			
Strawberry second																			
Sugar second																			
FIRST SCONE Banana first													
Black-currant first													
Blueberry first													
Pineapple first													
Strawberry first													
Sugar first													
FIRST NAMES Lowe							
Potter							
Robertson							
Symes							
Veness							
Willard							

Missing Script

Which number should replace the question mark, knowing that two-digit numbers are always shown?

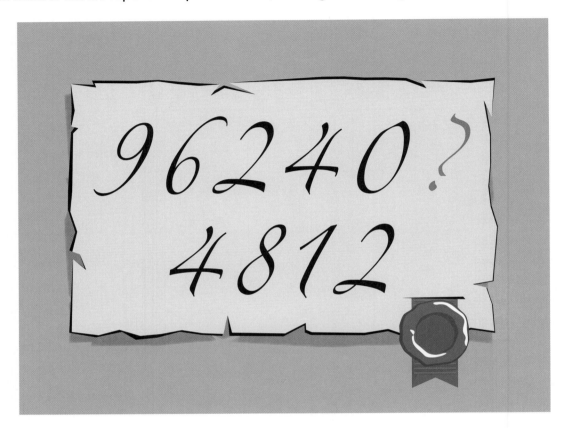

BLOCK ANAGRAM

Form the word that is described in the parentheses using the letters above the grid. Extra letters are already in the right place.

STONE AGE (large freshwater fish)

L		K				U	R			

CROSSWORD — Sandwich Shop

ACROSS

1 SESAC rival
6 Rowling's Beedle
10 Book after John
14 Culpability
15 Have ___ in one's bonnet
16 Loafer
17 New York City deli sandwich
19 Swiss marksman
20 Duelist's blade
21 Will in *The Campaign*
23 Fair maiden
26 Poltergeist signs
27 Stayed away from
29 Away from the action
30 Nursemaid
31 Left Bank river
33 To be, in Latin class
36 Minor detail
37 Luncheon sandwich
38 Aragon aunt
39 Couturier Cassini
41 Gumby's color
43 Colleague
44 "It" girl Bow
46 Boldly resistant
48 San ___ (Apennines republic)
50 Water pipe
51 Jennifer in *Just Go With It*
53 *East of Eden* brother
54 Party-giver
55 New Orleans sandwich
60 Der ___ (Adenauer)
61 Icelandic epic
62 Spine-tingling
63 Broadway beacon
64 Costly
65 Salon machine

DOWN

1 Diane Sawyer's network
2 Road sign
3 Airport rental
4 More than forgetfulness
5 Made like a chick
6 Baseball legend Ruth
7 Pappy Yokum's grandson
8 Coral Sea hazard
9 Goalie's job
10 On both sides of
11 Philly sandwich
12 *The Power of Now* author
13 NYSE orders
18 Removes, editorially
22 Versailles ruler
23 *Hawaii Five-O* nickname
24 Effective use
25 Fried ham-and-cheese sandwich
28 Winger in *Urban Cowboy*
29 Fed the kitty
32 Eugene O'Neill play
34 Italian city known for its clay
35 Universal logo
40 Glimmer
41 Like show dogs
42 Jacket for Dr. No
43 Davy Crockett, e.g.
45 Colony resident
47 Duped
48 2012 Shell Houston Open winner
49 American lizard
52 Art class figure
53 Long way off
56 Pill-approving org.
57 Word of encouragement
58 Haberdashery item
59 ___ Lingus airline

Beatlemania

ACROSS

1 Spice Girls hit
5 Rodin sculpture
9 Spay or neuter
14 Miner's entrance
15 *Bottled in Blonde* author Jaffe
16 Earth tone
17 1965 Beatles song
19 Where a king may be castled
20 New York's provincial neighbor
21 Vouch for
23 Cato's 104
24 Joe Hardy's steady
25 Platinum blond
29 "This way" signs
31 Feel (for)
32 Peter in *Beat the Devil*
34 "___ Song": Ringo Starr
36 Chinese pagoda
37 Pierre's assent
38 Blueprint
39 Range below soprano
41 Freddy Kruger, for one
43 Remove the skin
44 Has the same view
46 Wise
48 Pearl Buck character
49 Dr. with a *Detox* album
50 Unicorns and griffins
52 Show the ropes
56 "He ___ got a clue"
57 1964 Beatles song
59 Negative end of a battery
60 Get nosed out
61 No couch potato
62 Alfredo, in *La Traviata*
63 Unique fellow
64 "Waiting for the Robert ___"

DOWN

1 Clinic name
2 Mideast gulf
3 Waterfall sight
4 Briefcase
5 Timetable entry
6 Extinction exemplar
7 Tennis star Ivanovic
8 Builder of Chichén Itzá
9 No or Strangelove
10 Level of command
11 1964 Beatles song
12 At one time, at one time
13 Strikes (out)

18 Buffalo's lake
22 Spare item
25 "Good-bye, old chap!"
26 Florida horse city
27 1965 Beatles song
28 Portals
29 Prankster in *The Tempest*
30 Trap with a noose
33 Wish nullified
35 Newspaper page
40 Magic place?
41 Loafer coin
42 Huckster

43 Come before
45 Christian feast
47 Jack-in-the-pulpit
50 Cause of misery
51 Normandy commune
52 Extra
53 Military absentee
54 "... I ___ wed"
55 Thornfield Hall governess
56 Bowler
58 Long time

TRIVIA QUIZ Reel Them In!

Do you have what it takes to land a big one?
See how well you know your fish species with this watery round of true and false questions.

1. Walleyes are known for their marblelike eyes, which let them see well in dim light.
   a. true
   b. false

2. Trout are the only fish with an adipose fin (the small fin on the back just in front of the tail).
   a. true
   b. false

3. White and striped bass are members of the temperate bass family, as opposed to black bass, which belong to the sunfish family.
   a. true
   b. false

4. Flatheads are more apt to eat dead fish than any other catfish species.
   a. true
   b. false

5. The fry of all bass turn coal black within a few days after they hatch, but only the smallmouth bass stay that way, which is why they're referred to as black bass.
   a. true
   b. false

6. The white sturgeon, which is found in rivers along the Pacific Coast, will reach a weight of almost a ton.
   a. true
   b. false

7. Like pike, muskies feed actively throughout the year and are a popular target of ice fishermen.
   a. true
   b. false

8. Leeches are one of the top baits for walleyes.
   a. true
   b. false

9. Research has shown that a sudden decrease in light level triggers walleyes to bite.
   a. true
   b. false

10. Pike lose their teeth in the summer and don't bite.
    a. true
    b. false

trivia

• What type of fish is able to travel over land for extended periods of time?

_____

Mixed Drinks

ACROSS

1 Theda in *Cleopatra*
5 Benny's dog in *Rent*
10 Dick and Jane's dog
14 Yale attendees
15 Ocean motions
16 Toy on a string
17 Gin, lemon juice, sugar, and carbonated water
19 Mireille of *The Killing*
20 1972 David Bowie hit
21 Beat
23 B&B
24 Campus cadet org.
25 Lucky ___ foot
29 Upperclassmen
32 Having an off day
33 Sharp-tasting
35 Dragon nail
36 Sound from the crib
37 River in Switzerland
38 Gardner in *Mogambo*
39 Nile reptile
41 Avarice
43 Main port in Yemen
44 Under a roof
46 Indicators
48 Arizona city
49 Sardine whale
50 Raising, at the poker table
53 SAG president (1981–1985)
57 Lingual
58 Cocktail with mostly gin with a little vermouth
60 Fairy-tale fiend
61 Florida *CSI* setting
62 "I'll get right ___, boss!"
63 Grammy winner Alicia
64 Jordan capital
65 Stem joint

DOWN

1 They're taken at the track
2 Zillions
3 *Green Mansions* girl
4 Give credit to
5 Carter Library site
6 Clay oven
7 Uganda's Amin
8 Five will get you fifty
9 Confident
10 Questioning one
11 Strained pineapple
12 Great Plains Indians
13 Dick Tracy's love
18 Prefix meaning "all"
22 Weasley of Gryffindor
25 Christina in *Speed Racer*
26 Deck the halls
27 Cocktail containing tomato juice and vodka
28 Scuffle souvenirs
29 Fathers
30 *Boléro* composer
31 Long-necked beauties
34 Scottish explorer
40 Pairs
41 Nana
42 Derision
43 Jennifer in *Just Go With It*
45 Japan's largest lake
47 Paraphernalia
50 Libretto
51 Exhort
52 ___ Reaper
53 Uma's *Avengers* role
54 Senora's boy
55 Oklahoma city
56 Baptism, e.g.
59 Orange veggie

Sudoku

Fill in the grid so that each row, each column, and each 3 x 3 frame contains every number from 1 to 9.

	2			7	5	1	8	
		8		9		3		
	7			8				9
				4		9		
			7	3		2		
4			2		8		7	
		6	9					
	8	5						4

do you KNOW?

Where was
Georgia O'Keeffe
was born?

_____

SYMBOL SUMS

Can you work out these number sums using three of these four symbols? **+ − ÷ ×**

4 ☐ 2 ☐ 14 ☐ 7 = 21

Answers *(Do You Know? and Trivia answers are on page 224)*

Twitter Talk

D	A	T	E		S	L	A	V	E	D		L	S	D
E	W	A	N		H	E	L	E	N	A		E	T	O
B	E	S	T	R	E	G	A	R	D	S		T	E	T
T	E	T	R	A	D	S		A	U	T	O	M	A	T
S	K	E	E	T			R	A	R	E	L	Y		
		E	E	N	Y		D	E	R	E	K			
A	L	B		D	R	O	N	E		D	A	N	Z	A
B	O	Y	S		A	L	A	M	O		D	O	E	R
S	T	E	A	D		K	E	I	T	H		W	E	E
		F	L	I	P	S		T	E	E	S			
S	M	O	O	C	H				N	O	S	E	D	
T	U	R	N	K	E	Y		T	O	R	O	N	T	O
U	R	N		I	N	M	Y	O	P	I	N	I	O	N
F	R	O		E	O	C	E	N	E		E	D	N	A
F	E	W		S	L	A	T	E	D		R	E	S	T

Children

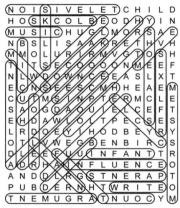

Childhood in humans is thought of as the magical period between birth and puberty.

Word Pyramid

I
(1) IT
(2) SIT
(3) SPIT
(4) STRIP
(5) PRIEST
(6) PIRATES
(7) PARASITE

More Twitter Talk

B	A	N	D		M	A	R	S	H	A		I	H	S
A	L	A	I		A	B	A	T	E	S		N	E	W
H	A	P	P	Y	T	O	H	E	L	P		R	I	O
T	E	A	P	O	T		S	E	M	I		E	D	O
P	O	W	D	E	R	E	D		T	E	A	L		
E	R	A		L	E	V	E	R		R	I	L	E	Y
R	A	N	T		D	E	L	O	S		L	I	V	E
U	L	T	R	A		L	E	A	P	T		F	E	N
		T	O	M	E		D	R	E	A	M	E	R	S
E	G	O	T	I	S	T		S	E	R	E			
N	U	S		A	T	O	M		C	O	M	M	A	S
D	I	E		B	E	R	I	G	H	T	B	A	C	K
E	L	L		L	E	S	S	E	E		E	C	R	U
D	E	L		E	M	O	T	E	S		R	H	E	A

Endings

1. cryptology—[C] study of codes (-ology = "study"). The Enigma code was cracked by aces in *cryptology*.

2. empathetic—[A] showing understanding or sensitivity (-pathy = "feeling"). Do you think women are more *empathetic* than men?

3. ovoid—[A] egg-shaped (-oid = "resembling"). Jay's *ovoid* physique made him a shoo-in for the role of Falstaff.

4. deify—[A] treat as a god (-fy = "make into"). First we *deify* pop stars, then we tear them down.

5. perspicacious—[B] of acute mental vision (-acious = "with a quality of"). She's too *perspicacious* to fall for their hoax.

6. indigenous—[B] native (-genous = "producing"). The protesters argued that chemical testing would disrupt the island's *indigenous* species.

7. herbicide—[C] agent used to inhibit or kill plant growth (-cide = "killing"). Mother Nature is not fond of lawn *herbicides*.

8. pachyderm—[A] elephant (-derm = "skin"). Cartoonist Thomas Nast drew the first Republican *pachyderm*.

9. Kafkaesque—[A] nightmarishly complex (-esque = "resembling"). Getting my passport back involved a *Kafkaesque* maze of bureaucracies.

10. atrophy—[A] waste away (-trophy = "nourishment"). Without rehab, Alison's knee will *atrophy*.

11. knavish—[C] deceitful or dishonest (-ish = "like"). OK, who's the *knavish* sneak who swiped my drink?

12. legalese—[C] legal language (-ese = "language style"). Please, cut the *legalese* and speak plain English.

13. patriarch—[B] father figure (-arch = "chief"). That loudmouth is the *patriarch* of all spin doctors.

14. obsolescent—[C] going out of use (-escent = "becoming"). Our landline is now *obsolescent*.

15. solarium—[A] sunroom (-arium = "place"). Let us retire to my *solarium* for a little more inspiration.

VOCABULARY RATINGS
9 and below: Linguist
10–12: Wordaholic
13–15: Brainiac

Cage the Animals

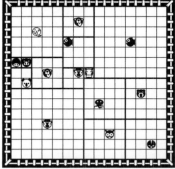

DELETE ONE • DELETE T AND FIND **NOAHS ARK**

FRIENDS • EACH CAN HAVE THE PREFIX HEAD- TO FORM A NEW WORD.

201

PAGE 14

When I Was 17 . . .

T	A	L	C		G	L	A	S	S		A	B	E	T
A	G	I	O		R	O	B	O	T		R	A	N	A
D	E	B	T		E	E	R	I	E		C	L	O	Y
S	E	R	E	N	A	W	I	L	L	I	A	M	S	
		E	R	A	S	E		S	L	E	D			
R	A	V	I	N	E			A	R	E	N	A	S	
E	L	I	E		D	E	T	E	R		S	O	D	A
A	L	L			M	E	L			V	A	T		
C	A	L	F		B	U	L	L	S		L	A	N	A
T	H	E	L	M	A			N	E	E	S	O	N	
		O	M	N	I		H	A	V	O	C			
M	A	R	I	A	S	H	A	R	A	P	O	V	A	
S	E	M	I		N	E	I	L	L		A	T	E	N
P	A	I	D		A	N	K	L	E		R	I	N	K
A	L	D	A		S	T	E	E	D		D	A	T	A

PAGE 15

Track and Field

They will all be together on line 19.

DOUBLETALK • BILLED/BUILD

PAGE 16

Bread and Cheese

1. Stilton
2. A pretzel
3. A goat
4. India
5. Spain
6. Cyprus
7. Ciabatta
8. India
9. Roquefort
10. Scotland or Ireland (a farl is a small cake or bread, either baked or cut into a triangular shape)
11. Wales
12. The Netherlands
13. Queso blanco (white cheese)
14. Brie

PAGE 17

Horoscope

DELETE ONE • DELETE E AND FIND **BEST-SELLING NOVEL**

FRIENDS • EACH CAN HAVE THE PREFIX FORE- TO FORM A NEW WORD

PAGE 18

Spot the Differences

PAGE 19

Well Positioned

B	A	W	D		W	O	M	A	N		C	R	O	P
A	B	E	E		I	N	A	N	E		H	I	R	E
T	O	P	B	I	L	L	I	N	G		O	G	L	E
T	O	T	A	L	L	Y		A	L	C	O	H	O	L
			C	S	A			E	A	S	T			
H	I	L	L	A	R	Y		S	C	R	E	A	M	S
O	S	E	E		D	E	P	O	T		S	N	I	P
O	A	F				A	O	L				G	N	U
P	A	T	S		C	R	E	A	M		C	L	E	M
S	C	H	O	O	L	S		N	O	W	H	E	R	E
		A	L	D	I				T	A	I			
C	O	N	D	E	M	N		S	I	R	L	O	I	N
L	O	D	I		B	O	T	T	O	M	L	I	N	E
A	L	E	E		E	D	W	I	N		E	L	L	E
P	A	R	R		R	E	A	R	S		D	Y	A	D

PAGE 20

Sport Maze

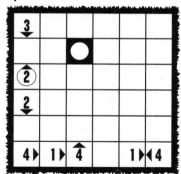

ONE LETTER LESS OR MORE • SANGRIA

PAGE 21

Sudoku

1	5	4	6	3	8	7	9	2
2	9	8	7	1	5	4	6	3
3	7	6	4	9	2	8	5	1
8	2	3	1	5	6	9	7	4
6	4	7	9	8	3	2	1	5
9	1	5	2	7	4	3	8	6
4	8	2	5	6	7	1	3	9
5	3	9	8	4	1	6	2	7
7	6	1	3	2	9	5	4	8

SYMBOL SUMS •
$33 - 15 \times 3 \div 6 = 9$

PAGE 22

Word Wheel

ANT, ART, RAT, TAN, TAR, AUNT, AURA, TARN, TUNA, ULNA, ALTAR, LUNAR, NATAL, TAUNT, ULTRA, TARTAN, TRUANT, NATURAL, TARANTULA.

Answers

Ones and Zeros

1100. After 0111 (7) comes 1000 (8). If you add 0100 (4) to it you get 1100 (12).

QUICK CROSSWORD •

	I				F		M		T
F	R	A	N	C	E		L I B Y A		O
	A		U		J		L		N
	Q		B	R	A	Z	I L		T O G O
	A		A				A		A

Population Group

Maori is the name of the people that inhabited New Zealand when it was discovered by Europeans.

Spooked

Number Fun 1

4	+	1	x	11	–	1	=	54
–	10	+	20	x	30	x		
3	–	2	+	6	x	12	=	84
+	40	x	50	–	60	–		
17	+	18	–	24	x	18	=	198
x	70	–	80	+	90	+		
4	x	31	+	7	–	41	=	90
=		=		=		=		
72		23		49		35		

DOODLE PUZZLE • Spills

Word Sudoku

G N T I R B S D A
D R S G A N B T I
B A I D S T G N R
T D R N B A I S G
I S G T D R A B N
A B N S G I D R T
S I B R T G N A D
N T D A I S R G B
R G A B N D T I S

UNCANNY TURN • SEPARATE

Oaters

Hourglass

(1) ENIGMAS
(2) IMAGES
(3) GAMES
(4) MEGA
(5) GATE
(6) AGENT
(7) EATING
(8) VINTAGE

Sunny

TRIANAGRAM • HALTERS/LATHERS

Horse Operas

Get in Gear

Direction B, counterclockwise.

DOODLE PUZZLE • BANANA SPLIT

PAGE 33

A Quick Dip

1. **a.** Anchor
2. **c.** Block
3. **b.** Gutter
4. **a.** Bow wave
5. **c.** Butterfly
6. **a.** Long-distance swimming
7. **b.** Prone
8. **b.** Center lanes
9. **b.** Flutter kick
10. **c.** Drag

PAGE 34

Theater

A musical is a play that uses a combination of play-acting, song, music and dance.

PAGE 35

Kakuro

DOUBLETALK • PORES/POURS

PAGE 36

Horse and Rider

PAGE 37

Number Cluster

DELETE ONE • DELETE S AND FIND **DEPARTMENT STORE**

SANDWICH • TIME

PAGE 38

Sudoku X

BLOCK ANAGRAM • MICHAEL PHELPS

PAGE 39

Bond Baddies

PAGE 40

Good Hand?

Card B, 5 of spades. The corners of A are not correct. C is already in the hand. D contains 9 diamonds instead of 7.

LETTER LINE • ELEMENTARY; REALM, ENAMEL, YEN, LAMENT, TAMELY

PAGE 41

Construction & Tools

1. **serrated**—[B] toothed like a saw. The fiery dragon's back was *serrated*, its claws razor-sharp.

2. **vise**—[A] clamp that holds an object in place. Before sanding the board, Louisa secured it in a *vise*.

3. **adze**—[A] ax-like tool with a curved blade. *Adzes* have been used to shape wood since the Stone Age.

4. **flanged**—[B] with a protruding rim. Bobby's model train has *flanged* wheels to keep it on the tracks.

5. **torque**—[A] twisting force. If you use the wrong *torque* setting on your drill, you could strip the screws.

6. **auger**—[B] spiral drill bit. To fish in the winter months, anglers use *augers* to bore holes in the ice.

Answers

7. dowel—[B] peg. Ethan decided to construct the birdhouse using wooden *dowels* instead of nails.

8. ferrule—[C] protective cap. Your hatchet's handle wouldn't have split if you'd braced it with a *ferrule*.

9. cambered—[B] arched. The highway is *cambered* in the middle to promote runoff of rain.

10. gauge—[C] measuring instrument. Christine used a homemade rain *gauge* to track the precipitation in her yard.

11. loupe—[C] magnifier. After examining the antique ring with his *loupe*, the appraiser determined the stone was glass.

12. awl—[A] pointed tool for piercing holes. Jerry used an *awl* to poke through the tough leather.

13. casters—[A] swiveling wheels. The heavy-duty *casters* on the dolly really helped make the move easier.

14. grommet—[A] ring that reinforces. Everything in Ashley's bathroom is pink, from the towels to the custom *grommets* she installed on the shower curtain.

15. kludge—[B] makeshift solution. I've patched together some of these cables; it's a bit of a *kludge*, but it just might work!

VOCABULARY RATINGS
9 & below: Apprentice
10–12: Artisan
13–15: Master

PAGE 42
Arf!

PAGE 43
Sport Maze

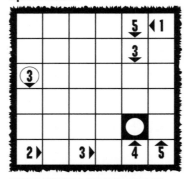

ONE LETTER LESS OR MORE • WARHEAD

PAGE 44
Flavors

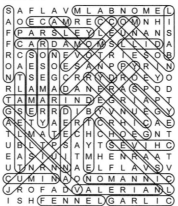

A flavor enhancer is a spice or an additive that accentuates the natural flavor of a dish.

PAGE 45
Cage the Animals

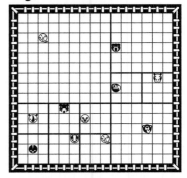

DELETE ONE • DELETE S AND ENJOY **ICE CREAM SUNDAES**

FRIENDS • EACH CAN HAVE THE PREFIX WAR- TO FORM A NEW WORD.

PAGE 46
Letter Shapes

E. Moving toward the center, the letters always have one more line.

DOODLE PUZZLE • RHYTHM AND BLUES

PAGE 47
Avian Look-alikes

PAGE 48

Face Value

1. Read as 8/2 = 4, 9/3 = 3, 6/1 = 6, 2/2 = 1.

QUICK WORD SEARCH •

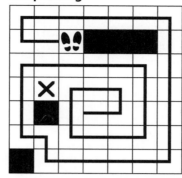

PAGE 49

Kakuro

8	1	4		3	2	4	8	1
9	3	7		7	1		9	8
	5	8	1	2		7	6	5
5	2		7	4	5	8	2	
6	4	1	9		2	9	7	1
7		2	8	1	7		5	4
8	9	7		2	1	4		8
9	7			3	1	8	2
2	5	4	1			8	9	6

DOUBLETALK • BOUGH/BOW

PAGE 50

Winning Hands

C	O	O	P		A	T	T	A	R		I	F	F	Y
A	F	R	O		T	R	I	B	E		M	U	L	E
P	A	I	R	O	F	A	C	E	S		P	L	E	A
E	G	O	T	R	I	P		T	U	T	E	L	A	R
D	E	N	I	E	R			M	A	T	H			
		C	O	S	T		T	E	N	U	O	U	S	
O	N	T	O		T	I	M	E	D		S	U	R	E
R	A	W		T	O	T				S	A	L		
C	R	O	P		F	L	O	R	A		C	E	L	L
A	C	Q	U	I	R	E		A	L	T	A			
	U	P	T	O				F	O	R	M	E	R	
D	E	E	P	E	S	T		B	R	O	M	I	D	E
O	N	E	I		T	H	R	E	E	K	I	N	G	S
A	N	N	E		E	A	S	E	D		N	E	A	T
S	A	S	S		D	I	T	T	O		E	R	R	S

PAGE 51

Keep Going

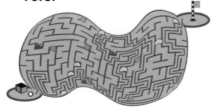

DELETE ONE: • DELETE S AND FIND YOURSELF **IN THE WILDERNESS**

PAGE 52

Noah's Ark

1. Emperor
2. Hibernaculum
3. Truffles
4. Good weather is on the way
5. A reptile; an Australian lizard
6. Formic acid
7. Shrimp
8. Mermaids' purses (or devils' purses)
9. The Romans
10. Black
11. The Goliath beetle or elephant beetle
12. The hippopotamus
13. Sloths
14. Bowhead whales

PAGE 53

Fore!

PAGE 54

Word Suduko

P	M	E	T	V	R	B	I	O
V	R	O	E	B	I	T	P	M
B	T	I	P	M	O	E	R	V
I	B	V	M	R	E	O	T	P
T	O	P	B	I	V	M	E	R
M	E	R	O	P	T	V	B	I
E	V	T	R	O	P	I	M	B
O	P	B	I	E	M	R	V	T
R	I	M	V	T	B	P	O	E

UNCANNY TURN • HUNTING

PAGE 55

Tiny Tots

B	A	S	S		C	R	E	E	P		T	B	A	R
A	L	E	E		H	I	L	L	S		R	A	L	E
B	E	A	N	I	E	B	A	B	Y		O	B	I	T
E	R	M	I	N	E	S		A	C	O	L	Y	T	E
S	T	Y	L	E	T			H	U	L	L			
		E	R	A	S		S	O	C	I	E	T	Y	
F	I	B		T	H	E	F	T		H	E	R	E	S
A	T	O	M		S	A	R	A	N		S	O	L	E
R	E	N	A	L		R	O	R	E	M		Y	E	R
R	A	U	C	O	U	S		K	I	A	S			
	S	H	U	N				G	R	E	A	S	E	
H	A	B	I	T	A	T		S	H	I	N	D	I	G
I	R	A	N		B	A	B	Y	B	O	O	M	E	R
G	I	B	E		L	L	A	N	O		R	A	V	E
H	A	Y	S		E	L	D	E	R		A	N	E	T

PAGE 56

Cube Location

C1. Identically colored cubes are stacked up.

DOUBLETALK • MUSTARD/ MUSTERED

Material

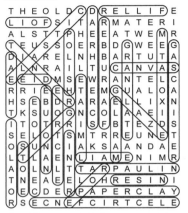

The oldest materials that were used were natural materials like tree trunks and animal hides.

Loves 1

A	D	A	R		T	R	I	A	D		M	G	B	S
R	I	L	E		R	A	N	G	E		E	U	R	O
M	A	I	D	M	A	R	I	A	N		R	I	E	N
E	N	G	R	A	V	E		T	I	E	R	N	E	Y
D	E	N	O	T	E		L	E	S	L	I	E		
		C	A	R	N	E		E	L	E	V	E	N	
P	A	C	K		S	E	A	R		A	R	E	N	A
A	L	L		M	E	A	D	O	W	S		R	I	M
L	I	E	G	E		T	S	A	R		M	E	D	E
S	T	O	L	E	S		I	R	E	N	A			
		P	I	S	T	O	N		T	O	T	T	E	R
A	M	A	T	E	U	R		A	C	H	I	E	V	E
M	A	T	T		P	O	C	A	H	O	N	T	A	S
I	N	R	E		I	N	U	R	E		E	R	N	E
R	E	A	R		D	O	T	E	D		E	A	S	T

The Impossible Room

Working from left to right, the errors are:

- I love NY embroidery shows a picture of the Eiffel Tower.
- Telephone (banana handset).

- Cushion on left of couch is made of concrete.
- Lampshade has no base.
- Window – shed is upside down; flower is too big; curtain has no tie.
- Wall switch has no button.
- Photo album is back to front.
- Tumbler on table is upside down.
- Bunch of grapes contains both green and black grapes.
- Glass top of table has only three supporting legs.
- Table is touching the floor at the back and floating at the front.
- Calendar shows Feb. 31 – Feb. has only 28 or 29 days.
- Chair has no wheels on its legs.
- Clock – back to front and has three hands.
- Computer mouse is a cartoon mouse.
- Wall map shows South America joined to Africa.
- Shadow of lampshade does not match shape of lamp.
- Bookcase – Romeo and Jeff; War and Peas; different door handles.

Going Bing's Way

1. May 3, 1903, Tacoma, Washington
2. "White Christmas"
3. Holiday Inn
4. "I'll Be Seeing You"
5. The Andrews Sisters
6. "Swinging on a Star"
7. The Bells of St. Mary's
8. *Road to Singapore* (1940)
   Road to Zanzibar (1941)
   Road to Morocco (1942)
   Road to Utopia (1946)
   Road to Rio (1947)
   Road to Bali (1952)
   The Road to Hong Kong (1962)

Sudoku Twin

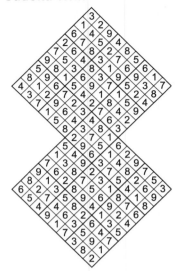

DELETE ONE • DELETE S AND FIND **SURGICAL INSTRUMENTS**

Spot the Differences

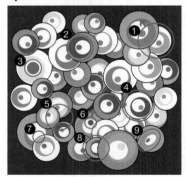

PAGE 63

Loves 2

A	M	O	S		F	E	A	T		F	E	R	A	L
B	A	T	T		I	N	C	H		O	V	O	L	O
A	P	H	R	O	D	I	T	E		R	A	C	E	R
C	L	E	A	N	E	D		R	E	A	C	H	E	D
K	E	R	N	E	L		D	E	N	G	U	E		
			G	R	I	M	E		S	E	E	S	A	W
B	A	B	E		T	A	F	T		R	E	T	I	E
A	L	E		C	Y	P	R	E	S	S		E	R	R
R	A	L	P	H		S	O	S	A		A	R	Y	E
R	E	L	O	A	D		S	T	U	D	S			
		A	R	R	E	S	T		T	A	S	S	E	L
I	N	S	T	A	N	T		G	E	N	U	I	N	E
R	E	W	E	D		A	N	D	R	O	M	E	D	A
I	N	A	N	E		L	E	A	N		E	N	O	S
S	E	N	D	S		K	A	Y	E		D	A	R	T

PAGE 64

Energy Saver

2 barrels. The number is always reversed, and the last number is dropped.

DOUBLETALK • BOLD/BOWLED

PAGE 65

Vocabulary-building

1. capitulate—[B] stop resisting. Only when I wrapped the pill in bacon did my dog finally *capitulate*.

2. unequivocal—[C] leaving no doubt. The ump unleashed a resonant, *unequivocal* "Steee-rike!"

3. cavalier—[A] nonchalant or marked by disdainful dismissal. Our driver had a shockingly *cavalier* attitude about the steep mountain road ahead.

4. leery—[A] untrusting. Initially, Eve was a touch *leery* of the apple.

5. levity—[B] merriment. Our family thankfully found moments of *levity* during the memorial.

6. penchant—[B] strong liking. Thomas was warned repeatedly about his *penchant* for daydreaming in meetings.

7. bifurcate—[C] divide into parts. If anything, Donald Trump has certainly managed to *bifurcate* the nation.

8. craven—[C] cowardly. She took a markedly *craven* position against the weak crime bill.

9. coterie—[A] exclusive group. Claire's *coterie* consisted entirely of fellow Mozart enthusiasts and violinists.

10. stalwart—[A] loyal. Throughout the senator's campaign, Kerrie has repeatedly shown *stalwart* support.

11. travesty—[C] absurd imitation. Her lawyer demanded an appeal, calling the jury's decision a *travesty* of justice.

12. hedonism—[C] pursuit of pleasure. In Shakespeare's *Henry IV,* young Prince Hal mistakes *hedonism* for heroism.

13. obviate—[B] prevent or render unnecessary. Gloria's doctor hoped that physical therapy would *obviate* the need for more surgery.

14. excoriate—[B] criticize harshly. Coach Keegan was *excoriated* by the media for the play calling during the game's final minutes.

15. penurious—[C] poor. Paul and Carla entered the casino flush and left it *penurious*.

VOCABULARY RATINGS

9 & below: Prodigy
10–12: Mental giant
13–15: Genius

PAGE 66

Inside Man

M	E	G	A		S	A	S	H	A		S	C	A	N
O	N	E	R		L	I	N	E	S		H	O	L	E
P	Y	R	O	M	A	N	I	A	C		O	M	E	R
S	A	M	U	E	L		P	R	E	S	U	M	E	D
			S	T	O	P		A	N	I	T	A		
R	E	D	E	E	M	E	R		T	R	I	N	A	L
A	N	I		S	E	D	E	R		E	N	D	U	E
B	U	S	S		D	A	N	E	S		G	E	N	T
A	R	M	E	D		L	E	N	T	O		E	T	H
T	E	A	P	O	T		W	A	R	H	O	R	S	E
		N	A	R	E	S		L	E	A	P			
E	N	T	R	A	N	C	E		A	R	I	O	S	O
F	A	L	A		S	A	L	A	M	A	N	D	E	R
T	R	E	T		E	L	A	T	E		E	I	R	E
S	A	D	E		D	E	T	E	R		D	E	A	L

PAGE 67

Scrappy Scarecrow

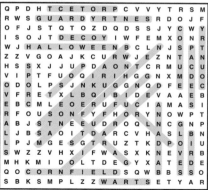

PAGE 68

Sport Maze

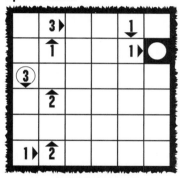

ONE LETTER LESS OR MORE • VINTAGE

PAGE 69

Outside Man

L	A	M	B		T	R	I	E	S		G	M	E	N
I	R	A	E		H	E	A	V	E		R	A	R	E
M	I	D	S	H	I	P	M	A	N		E	T	T	E
N	E	E	S	O	N		A	N	I	M	A	T	E	D
			I	N	K	S		S	L	A	T	E		
C	O	M	E	D	I	A	N		E	M	E	R	G	E
R	P	I		A	N	G	U	S		A	S	H	E	N
E	R	N	S		G	A	B	L	E		T	O	N	E
S	A	N	T	A		L	I	O	N	S		R	I	M
T	H	E	R	M	S		A	T	T	O	R	N	E	Y
		S	U	I	T	S		H	I	F	I			
P	R	O	T	R	A	C	T		R	A	P	I	D	S
R	I	T	T		M	A	S	T	E	R	P	L	A	N
A	L	A	E		P	L	A	I	T		E	S	N	E
M	E	N	D		S	P	R	A	Y		D	E	K	E

Answers

In the Know with Nutrition

1. Beans are not a complete protein
2. Cholesterol
3. Milk sugar and fruit sugar
4. More
5. Water
6. Olive oil
7. Nutrition
8. Amino acids
9. Gluten
10. Protein
11. Calories
12. 21 to 35 grams
13. Cheese
14. Vitamin B-12 is stored in the liver

Word Sudoku

G	N	T	Y	R	L	A	H	S
Y	A	H	G	N	S	L	T	R
R	S	L	A	T	H	Y	G	N
A	R	G	L	H	Y	N	S	T
N	L	S	T	A	R	G	Y	H
T	H	Y	S	G	N	R	L	A
H	Y	A	R	S	G	T	N	L
L	T	N	H	Y	A	S	R	G
S	G	R	N	L	T	H	A	Y

UNCANNY TURN • TRAFFIC LIGHTS

Sewing Basket

Cabin Fever

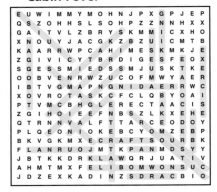

Number Cluster

DELETE ONE • DELETE S AND FIND **A NIGHT TO REMEMBER**

SANDWICH • WATER

Blues Singers

R	A	M	P		S	C	A	D	S		P	L	O	T
E	L	I	A		H	A	V	O	C		Y	E	T	I
F	A	T	S	D	O	M	I	N	O		R	A	T	E
S	E	E	S	A	W	S		E	L	E	A	N	O	R
		A	L	I			D	A	M	N				
L	O	D	G	I	N	G		R	E	T	I	R	E	S
I	R	A	E		G	A	P	E	D		D	I	S	C
L	I	V			R	A	F				M	T	A	
L	E	I	S		A	R	M	E	D		F	E	E	L
E	L	D	E	R	L	Y		R	E	V	I	S	E	D
		B	R	E	T			P	E	N				
S	T	O	P	P	E	R		H	A	R	D	E	N	S
L	O	W	E		R	O	Y	O	R	B	I	S	O	N
E	R	I	N		E	V	E	R	T		N	A	R	A
D	I	E	T		D	E	A	N	S		G	U	M	P

Furniture

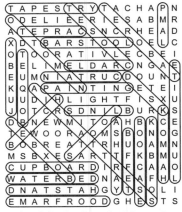

A chandelier is a branched decorative ceiling-mounted light fixture with two or more arms bearing lights.

Keep Going

PAGE 78

Futoshiki

4	5	3	1	2
5	1	4	2	3
2	4 < 5	3	1
1	3 > 2	5	4
3 > 2	1	4 < 5

LETTERBLOCKS • DEALER/ SHUFFLE

PAGE 79

Sunny

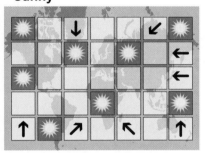

TRIANAGRAM • LUMPS/PLUMS

PAGE 80

More Than a Walk

S	P	A	C	E		S	H	U	E		T	R	A	P
T	E	T	O	N		H	E	L	M		R	I	D	E
I	R	O	N	S		A	R	N	O		E	T	O	N
R	U	N	N	I	N	G	B	A	T	T	L	E	S	
		E	G	O				I	A	L				
E	T	E	R	N	A	L		N	O	T	I	O	N	S
D	U	T	Y		H	U	R	O	N		S	N	I	T
D	N	A			R	U	B					I	T	E
Y	I	P	E		C	A	R	L	S		Y	O	R	E
S	C	E	N	E	R	Y		E	L	E	A	N	O	R
		G	E	O				A	N	C				
	G	A	L	L	O	P	I	N	G	G	H	O	S	T
D	E	M	I		K	I	T	E		A	T	L	A	S
E	N	O	S		E	P	I	C		G	E	E	N	A
W	A	S	H		D	E	S	K		E	D	G	A	R

PAGE 81

Lucky Number

22. In each following grid the numbers from the previous grid are decreased by one: 6-9-17-24-34 becomes 5-8-16-23-33 in the second grid and 4-7-15-22-32 in the last grid.

DOUBLETALK • FLOUR/FLOWER

PAGE 82

Sport Maze

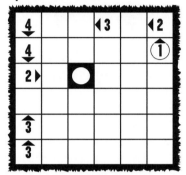

ONE LETTER LESS OR MORE • DISAPPEAR

PAGE 83

Football Season

N	O	T	E	S		F	A	D		S	A	C
F	R	O	S	T		I	N	N		P	R	O
L	A	N	K	A		S	T	A	D	I	U	M
		I	R	A	T	E		R	E	B	A	
H	E	L	M	E	T		M	E	S	A	S	
O	L	E	O		O	C	T	O				
P	I	G		A	L	O	U	D		I	G	A
			B	L	O	T		S	N	A	G	
B	A	S	I	C		T	A	C	K	L	E	
O	D	O	R		A	T	I	M	E			
D	E	F	E	N	S	E		A	N	N	O	Y
E	L	A		A	I	R		S	I	R	E	D
D	E	S		B	A	M		S	C	A	R	S

PAGE 84

Against the Clock

39 seconds. This is the formula: 15 + (1 + 5) = 21 + (2 + 1) = 24 + (2 + 4) = 30 + (3 + 0) = 33 + (3 + 3) = 39.

QUICK WORD SEARCH •

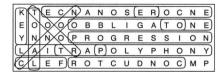

PAGE 85

Doctor, Doctor

1. Aspirin, which is derived from substances found in willow bark (cricket bats are traditionally made of willow)
2. Someone with asthma
3. Acupuncture
4. Foxglove (digitalis)
5. X-rays
6. Penicillin
7. Homeopathy
8. Stroke and thrombosis; it's an anticoagulant
9. Heart and lung transplants
10. Laughing gas—a painkiller
11. 206
12. Ileum
13. Jaundice
14. Tooth enamel

PAGE 86

The Billionaire Club

P	L	O	D		P	L	U	S		C	A	B	A	L
E	I	N	E		O	A	R	S		A	M	I	G	O
S	T	E	V	E	W	Y	N	N		S	E	L	E	S
T	H	I	E	V	E	S		S	C	A	R	L	E	T
S	E	L	L	E	R			A	B	I	G			
			O	N	E	S		N	I	A	G	A	R	A
P	U	L	P		D	I	V	A	N		O	T	I	C
A	L	A			D	I	D				E	T	E	
I	N	R	E		E	L	C	I	D		T	S	A	R
N	A	R	R	A	T	E		A	U	T	O			
		Y	O	D	A			K	A	N	S	A	S	
C	A	P	S	U	L	E		C	A	L	G	A	R	Y
A	V	A	I	L		M	A	R	K	C	U	B	A	N
G	I	G	O	T		M	L	I	I		E	R	G	O
E	D	E	N	S		A	L	B	S		S	E	E	D

Answers

The Adventures of Tintin

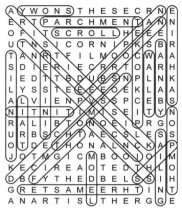

The Secret of the Unicorn is a film directed by Steven Spielberg, based on a comic book created by the Belgian artist Hergé

Sudoku

7	4	1	9	6	3	8	2	5
2	6	5	7	4	8	1	9	3
9	3	8	1	5	2	7	6	4
4	8	9	6	3	7	2	5	1
6	1	3	2	8	5	4	7	9
5	2	7	4	9	1	6	3	8
1	7	4	5	2	9	3	8	6
3	9	2	8	1	6	5	4	7
8	5	6	3	7	4	9	1	2

SYMBOL SUMS •
$3 \div 3 \times 18 - 9 = 9$

4-Syllable Words 1

H	A	L	S		A	L	A	M	O		K	H	A	N
E	D	I	T		R	E	L	I	C		R	A	C	E
I	M	P	O	S	S	I	B	L	E		E	R	M	A
D	A	I	R	I	E	S		S	L	A	M	M	E	R
I	N	D	I	A	N			O	R	L	O			
			E	M	I	T		S	T	R	I	N	G	S
A	D	D	S		C	O	L	T	S		N	I	L	E
L	I	I			M	I	R				C	U	T	
B	O	S	C		H	A	Z	E	L		R	A	M	S
A	R	C	A	D	E	S		P	E	L	E			
	O	L	E	A			S	E	C	U	R	E		
R	E	V	O	L	V	E		M	O	N	I	T	O	R
O	V	E	R		I	N	V	I	T	A	T	I	O	N
T	E	R	I		E	D	I	T	H		A	L	M	S
A	R	Y	E		R	O	M	E	O		L	E	S	T

Wheeling Around

E. The cyclists always ride to cities where the first letters form TOUR DE FRANCE.

LETTER LINE • TOURNAMENT;
REMNANT, NEUTRON, TANTRUM, MANNER, TORMENT

Language of Love

1. ardent—[C] passionate. Though he's a native New Yorker, Peter is an *ardent* Red Sox fan.

2. paramour—[B] lover. Claire was overwhelmed by the devotion and affection of her new *paramour*.

3. buss—[A] kiss. During the bus ride, Lauren and Alex sneaked off to *buss* in the backseat.

4. swain—[B] male suitor. The princess gave a weary sigh as she awaited the entreaties of her *swains*.

5. connubial—[B] of marriage. Aside from their celebrity status, Paul Newman and Joanne Woodward were famous for their *connubial* bliss.

6. troth—[B] fidelity. "It was in this gazebo, 20 years ago, dear, that we pledged our *troth*," said Arthur.

7. coquettish—[A] flirtatious. Alison caught Dean's eye with a *coquettish* smile and nod.

8. macushla—[A] darling. In *Million Dollar Baby*, boxing trainer Clint Eastwood gave his dear protégé Hilary Swank the nickname *macushla*.

9. platonic—[C] without physical desire. I hate to disappoint the paparazzi, but my current relationships are all *platonic*.

10. liaison—[A] secret affair. The young couple stole away at midnight each evening for their *liaison*.

11. beaux—[C] boyfriends. I doubt that Sharon considers young Timothy one of her best *beaux*.

12. requite—[B] give back, as affection. Her lyrics tend toward *requited* love rather than heartbreak.

13. epistolary—[C] relating to letters. The romance between Elizabeth Barrett Browning and Robert Browning is marked by an *epistolary* trail.

14. philter—[A] love potion. Hoping for attention from my crush, I went to Madam Ava for her purported *philter*.

15. cupidity—[B] lust or desire for wealth. The testimony gave clear evidence of the *cupidity* of the accused investors.

VOCABULARY RATINGS
9 & below: Flirty
10–12: Affectionate
13–15: Amorous

4-Syllable Words 2

PAGE 93

Concentration—One Liner

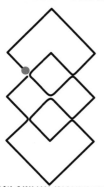

MARRIAGEABILITY, INAUSPICIOUS, LIFEGUARD, TIPTOE, DEN

PAGE 94

Sunny

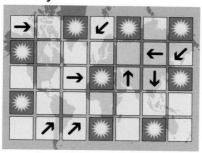

TRIANAGRAM • LAMPS/PALMS

PAGE 95

4-Syllable Words 3

S	P	E	C		F	E	E	D		T	R	A	G	G
N	O	A	H		E	L	L	E		S	E	L	M	A
I	N	V	I	S	I	B	L	E		H	A	L	E	Y
T	E	E	N	A	G	E		R	A	I	S	I	N	
		E	I	N			F	R	O	G				
B	O	B	S	L	E	D		C	A	T	N	A	P	
O	B	I	E		D	E	T	E	R		S	T	A	B
P	E	N			S	O	L				O	D	E	
P	L	O	D		L	E	V	E	R		I	R	M	A
I	C	E	B	O	X		B	E	R	N	S	E	N	
	U	F	O	S			V	I	S					
S	L	E	U	T	H		D	E	N	T	I	S	T	
S	L	A	N	G		E	M	E	R	G	E	N	C	Y
M	A	R	S	H		R	O	L	E		A	S	A	P
U	P	S	E	T		B	O	L	D		D	O	T	E

PAGE 96

Hourglass

(1) KISSING
(2) SKIING
(3) KINGS
(4) SINK
(5) SPIN
(6) SPAIN
(7) PIANOS
(8) PASSION

PAGE 97

Relationships

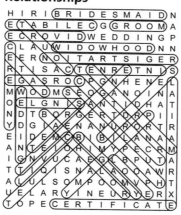

Hiring a wedding planner is a phenomenon that originated in America but is now also popular in Europe.

PAGE 98

Winter Solstice

Y	U	L	E		B	O	W		C	O	L	A
E	R	I	N		E	V	E		A	R	A	B
W	A	N	D		D	A	R	K	N	E	S	S
S	L	E	E	P		L	E	I	A			
		A	I	L			A	D	E	L	E	
S	H	O	R	T	E	S	T		A	G	U	A
W	E	T		T	A	K	E	I		A	N	S
A	R	I	D		F	I	R	S	T	D	A	Y
B	E	S	E	T		N	N	W				
	L	O	O	K		T	I	R	E	S		
D	E	C	E	M	B	E	R		S	U	L	K
E	R	A	T		O	N	E		T	I	M	E
W	A	V	E		E	T	C		S	N	O	W

PAGE 99

Sweet Thing

Candy 8. There are two types of candy with alternating colored grains, yellow-red and yellow-blue. The color alternates every two grains on candy 8.

WORD WALL • CHARACTERISTICALLY, ELECTROMAGNETIC, PRECIPITATED, FATALISTS, BOMBED, APE

PAGE 100

Sport Maze

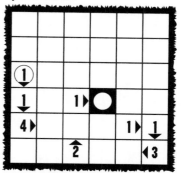

ONE LETTER LESS OR MORE • ASPIRIN

PAGE 101

Futoshiki

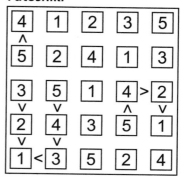

LETTERBLOCKS • CYCLONE/MONSOON

Answers

Sudoku

8	4	6	9	2	1	3	5	7
5	7	2	3	6	4	9	8	1
9	3	1	8	5	7	4	6	2
6	2	4	7	8	3	1	9	5
7	1	9	5	4	2	8	3	6
3	5	8	1	9	6	7	2	4
1	9	5	6	7	8	2	4	3
2	8	3	4	1	5	6	7	9
4	6	7	2	3	9	5	1	8

SYMBOL SUMS •
$9 \times 5 - 3 \div 6 = 7$

Flags with Circles

P	A	S	O		L	A	T	C	H		O	M	A	R
A	L	P	S		I	S	E	R	E		B	A	R	E
S	O	U	T	H	K	O	R	E	A		S	C	A	N
T	E	R	R	I	E	R		P	L	A	C	E	B	O
A	S	S	I	G	N		S	T	E	W	E	D		
			C	H	E	A	T		D	O	N	O	R	S
S	I	G	H		S	N	A	P		K	E	N	Y	A
H	O	R		A	S	T	R	I	D	E		I	A	N
I	N	E	P	T		S	T	L	O		G	A	N	G
P	E	E	R	E	D		E	L	L	I	E			
		N	E	A	R	E	D		P	R	O	S	I	T
P	U	L	L	M	A	N		C	H	O	R	I	N	E
E	S	A	U		W	A	S	H	I	N	G	T	O	N
R	E	N	D		E	T	H	A	N		I	A	N	D
M	E	D	E		R	E	E	D	S		A	R	E	S

Fore!

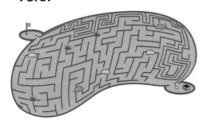

Good Grief!

1. Charlie Brown
2. Lucy Van Pelt
3. Linus Van Pelt
4. Beethoven
5. The Little Red-Haired Girl
6. Peppermint Patty
7. Woodstock
8. 5 cents
9. The Red Baron
10. Pigpen
11. Woodstock's name wasn't revealed until the early 1970s, after the 1969 Woodstock music festival.
12: October 30

Flags with Stars

P	A	N	G		C	H	I	D	E		S	A	S	S
A	R	E	A		H	E	L	E	N		T	U	T	U
N	E	W	Z	E	A	L	A	N	D		A	S	O	R
I	N	T	E	R	I	M		S	E	A	T	T	L	E
C	A	S	T	O	R		E	A	G	E	R			
			T	O	M	E	S		R	E	L	A	T	E
S	A	V	E		A	R	C	A		D	Y	L	A	N
T	E	E		N	O	R	M	S			I	C	Y	
E	R	N	S	T		S	U	I	T		C	A	T	O
P	O	E	T	I	C		B	E	E	C	H			
	Z	E	R	O	S			A	L	A	N	I	S	
S	H	U	T	O	U	T		E	L	E	G	A	N	T
P	I	E	S		P	U	E	R	T	O	R	I	C	O
A	R	L	O		O	P	R	A	H		I	V	A	N
S	T	A	N		N	A	S	T	Y		N	E	N	E

More Sweet Things

Lollipop 5. For all the other lollipops, the second and fourth ring starting from the outer edge are identical colors.

QUICK CROSSWORD •

	C		A	N	G	R	Y						
	L		C						T	I	G	H	T
S	E	R	I	O	U	S		H				R	
	A		D		A			I	L	L		U	
D	R	Y		S	U	D	D	E	N		W	E	T

Word Sudoku

B	F	I	N	D	M	O	A	T
T	A	M	O	F	B	N	D	I
O	N	D	T	A	I	B	M	F
N	T	O	M	B	D	I	F	A
A	D	B	F	I	T	M	N	O
M	I	F	A	O	N	D	T	B
F	O	N	B	M	A	T	I	D
D	B	T	I	N	F	A	O	M
I	M	A	D	T	O	F	B	N

UNCANNY TURN • WORTH TEA

Historic Figures

D	U	M	B	O		A	B	A	T		P	L	A	N
I	T	A	L	O		D	E	M	I		L	O	R	E
S	A	L	A	D		A	R	A	M		U	S	E	S
C	H	A	R	L	E	S	T	H	E	G	R	E	A	T
		N	E	T			C	I	A					
F	O	R	E	S	T	S		P	O	L	L	U	T	E
A	H	O	Y		E	Q	U	I	P		S	K	I	M
N	A	P			U	R	L				A	R	M	
G	R	E	W		Y	I	E	L	D		A	S	E	A
S	E	D	A	T	E	D		S	A	D	N	E	S	S
		S	R	A			T	O	T					
R	I	C	H	A	R	D	T	H	E	T	H	I	R	D
U	G	L	I		N	A	R	A		T	O	M	E	I
T	E	E	N		E	D	E	N		E	N	A	T	E
S	T	A	G		D	E	E	D		D	Y	N	E	S

Spot the Differences

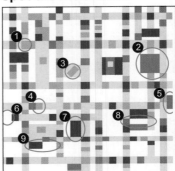

PAGE 111

Laboratory

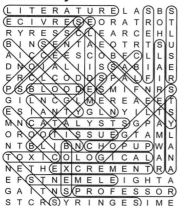

Laboratory research into traces of DNA is becoming increasingly important in the fight against crime.

PAGE 112

Binairo

I	O	I	I	O	O	I	O	O	I	I	O
I	I	O	O	I	O	I	I	O	O	I	O
O	I	I	O	O	I	O	I	I	O	O	I
O	O	I	I	O	I	I	O	O	I	I	O
I	I	O	I	I	O	O	I	O	O	I	O
O	O	I	O	I	I	O	O	I	O	I	I
I	O	O	I	O	I	I	O	I	O	I	O
I	I	O	O	I	O	I	O	I	O	I	O
O	O	I	I	O	O	I	O	I	I	O	I
O	I	O	O	I	I	O	I	I	O	I	O
I	I	O	I	O	O	I	O	O	I	O	I
O	O	I	O	I	I	O	I	I	O	O	I

TRIANAGRAM • DIRER/DRIER

PAGE 113

Back to School

1. parochial—[C] run by a church. Years of wearing *parochial* school uniforms left me hating plaid.

2. conscientious—[A] extremely careful. Carly is so *conscientious*— this sloppy book report isn't like her.

3. pore—[B] study intently. Sam *pored* over his European history notes the night before the midterm.

4. carrel—[A] library nook. In graduate school, I'd practically sleep in a *carrel* before final exams.

5. curriculum—[C] set of courses. The first class in Pierre's cooking *curriculum* is Sauces, Soups, and Stews.

6. pedantic—[B] making a show of knowledge. Professor Riordon knows a lot, but I find his bookish teaching style a bit *pedantic*.

7. glean—[C] gather. From what I *glean* from her essays, Shauna has done a lot of traveling.

8. rudiments—[C] beginner's skills. First-year students at Hogwarts must learn the *rudiments* of wizardry.

9. syntax—[B] sentence structure. This sentence a rather tortured *syntax* has.

10. semantic—[A] related to meaning in language. "What's the *semantic* difference between *clown* and *fool*?" our English teacher asked.

11. pedagogy—[A] art of teaching. "There are no lucrative awards for *pedagogy*," said Mr. Wilcox, "but I find it very rewarding."

12. syllabus—[B] class outline. This *syllabus* has no homework assignments listed—woo-hoo!

13. woolgathering—[C] daydreaming. If you hadn't been *woolgathering* in class, you wouldn't have flunked.

14. cognizant—[B] aware. "I'm *cognizant* of the facts of your case," the vice-principal told Mason, "but they don't excuse cheating."

15. empirical—[C] based on observation. Brody's science project presents *empirical* evidence that eating chocolate is good for you.

VOCABULARY RATINGS
9 & below: Pupil
10–12: Scholar
13–15: Professor

PAGE 114

Halloween Fun

G	R	A	B		M	A	Z	E		S	H	E
A	U	T	O		E	D	E	N		H	E	S
S	T	A	B		L	A	N	T	E	R	N	S
			B	U	O	Y		E	L	E	N	A
E	N	S	I	G	N		F	R	I	D	A	Y
B	E		I	N	G		H	I	S			
B	E	R	G		O	A	T		C	A	R	A
		E	R	G		Y	O	K	E	L		
D	E	L	U	X	E		S	E	S	A	M	E
A	R	E	S	O		O	A	S	T			
T	R	E	A	T	I	N	G		U	R	G	E
E	E	K		I	D	E	A		M	O	A	T
R	D	S		C	O	R	N		E	M	M	A

PAGE 115

Rain or Shine

Symbol 1. Starting at the bottom, the symbols are added per two (see line 4 to line 3). If two identical symbols come together, then that symbol disappears (see line 3 to line 2).

DOUBLETALK • BE/BEE

PAGE 116

Sudoku X

7	5	8	9	4	3	2	1	6
2	1	4	6	8	5	9	7	3
9	3	6	1	7	2	5	8	4
8	6	2	5	1	9	3	4	7
1	9	5	7	3	4	6	2	8
3	4	7	2	6	8	1	5	9
6	2	1	8	9	7	4	3	5
5	8	3	4	2	6	7	9	1
4	7	9	3	5	1	8	6	2

BLOCK ANAGRAM • MAHE DRYSDALE

PAGE 117

Tricolor Flags

B	O	S	S	A		K	E	B	A	B		I	M	A
A	V	I	A	N		O	R	O	N	O		V	E	T
N	E	T	H	E	R	L	A	N	D	S		O	N	O
D	R	E	A	M	O	N		N	O	S	T	R	U	M
		R	I	P				V	E	R	Y			
S	O	L	A	C	E	D		M	E	D	I	C	A	L
A	R	U	N		S	O	F	A	R		P	O	L	Y
N	I	X		R	E	V				A	A	R
T	E	E	M		M	I	N	E	D		E	S	T	E
A	L	M	A	N	A	C		N	E	G	A	T	E	S
		B	R	A	G			B	O	S				
O	P	O	S	S	U	M		O	R	A	T	I	O	N
L	O	U		S	I	E	R	R	A	L	E	O	N	E
E	R	R		E	R	I	C	A		I	R	W	I	N
S	K	G		R	E	N	A	L		E	N	A	T	E

PAGE 118

Fabulously Fashionable

1. Paris Hilton
2. Parsons
3. Fashion Week
4. Project Runway
5. Madrid
6. Victoria Beckham
7. Coco Chanel
8. Richard Avedon
9. Anna Wintour
10. Barney's
11. Diane von Furstenberg
12. Furs

PAGE 119

Wax Works

Monday – 450, red, knights
Tuesday – 750, green, rooks
Wednesday – 500, orange, bishops
Thursday – 600, yellow, queens
Friday – 700, white, pawns.

Yellow candles were made on Thursday (clue 2), so (clue 3) knight-shaped candles were made on Monday, green candles on Tuesday and 500 orange candles on Wednesday. The knights are red (4). By elimination, white candles were made on Friday. Ivor made either 600 queens and 450 knights (4) or 750 queens and 600 knights. Thus, the batch of 600 were either queens or knights. So (2) 700 pawns and 600 yellow candles were made. Since knights are red (above), he made 450 knights and (4) 600 queens. Knights were made on Monday (above), so (1) 700 candles were made on Friday. By a process of elimination, we can work out that 750 were made on Tuesday. Tuesday's batch wasn't bishops (1), so must have been rooks. Bishops were made on Wednesday. Thus: Monday – 450, red, knights; Tuesday – 750, green, rooks; Wednesday – 500, orange, bishops; Thursday – 600, yellow, queens; Friday – 700, white, pawns.

PAGE 120

Themeless 1

W	E	A	N	S		E	Z	R	A		W	I	L	E
A	L	L	O	T		W	E	A	R		A	N	I	L
R	E	P	R	E	S	E	N	T	A	T	I	V	E	S
D	E	S	E	R	T	S		S	P	O	K	A	N	E
			P	E	E		A	R	I	L				
H	O	L	L	O	W	S		T	H	E	K	I	N	G
A	H	O	Y		S	A	N	Y	O		I	D	O	L
V	A	N			C	A	P			A	V	I
O	R	E	L		G	R	E	E	N		S	T	A	N
C	A	R	A	B	O	O		S	O	F	T	E	S	T
		A	C	E	D		H	O	O					
S	A	N	T	A	F	E		T	O	R	M	E	N	T
S	I	G	O	U	R	N	E	Y	W	E	A	V	E	R
T	R	E	S		E	Y	E	R		S	C	E	N	E
S	E	R	E		Y	O	N	O		T	H	R	E	E

PAGE 121

Sunny

TRIANAGRAM • NEAREST/ EARNEST

PAGE 122

Word Sudoku

UNCANNY TURN • RENEWAL

PAGE 123

Color Coordinated

T	E	M	P		N	O	L	A	N		S	G	T	S
E	S	A	I		O	R	O	N	O		U	R	A	L
D	A	R	T	H	V	A	D	E	R		S	E	M	I
S	U	C	C	E	E	D		T	E	M	P	E	S	T
			H	A	L			P	E	E	N			
E	S	T	E	L	L	E		P	L	A	C	A	T	E
L	A	H	R		A	L	L	A	Y		T	R	A	M
I	L	E			T	Y	S			R	U	B
A	M	P	S		C	O	N	T	E		M	O	P	E
S	A	H	A	R	A	N		A	L	L	O	W	E	D
		A	B	E	L			E	A	T				
H	E	N	R	E	I	D		A	G	I	T	A	T	E
A	C	T	I		S	A	N	T	A	C	L	A	U	S
M	O	O	N		T	W	E	E	N		E	R	R	S
A	L	M	A		A	N	E	N	T		D	E	K	E

PAGE 124

Number Series

8. The numbers are running in a descending sequence of 9–1. Where a number does not fit in with the sequence, it is added to the next number, but if the pair does not fit in with the sequence, then the first number is erased. The reasoning reads as follows: 9, 8 (made from 4 + 4), 7, 6 (made from 5 + 1), 5, 4 (made from 3 + 1), 3, 2 (made from 1 + 1), 1

LETTER LINE • **APOSTROPHE;** TROOPS, PERHAPS, SHAPE, SPEAR, PHOTOS

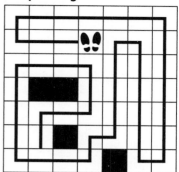

PAGE 125

Sudoku

2	3	7	9	4	1	5	6	8
8	1	5	6	7	3	9	2	4
9	4	6	5	8	2	7	1	3
6	8	1	7	5	9	4	3	2
3	7	2	1	6	4	8	9	5
4	5	9	2	3	8	1	7	6
1	2	8	4	9	6	3	5	7
5	9	3	8	2	7	6	4	1
7	6	4	3	1	5	2	8	9

SYMBOL SUMS •
$16 + 8 − 2 ÷ 2 = 11$

PAGE 126

Themeless 2

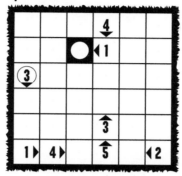

PAGE 127

Hair Salon

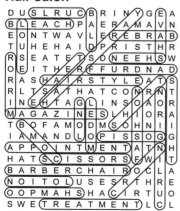

During a permanent wave, the hair is treated with a salt that contains a lot of ammonia and that causes the hair to swell.

PAGE 128

Sport Maze

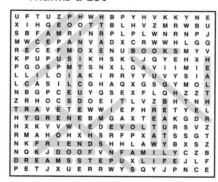

ONE LETTER LESS OR MORE •
INTRODUCE

PAGE 129

Thanks a Lot

(word search grid)

PAGE 130

Keep Going

**DELETE ONE • DELETE S AND BE
AIR CONDITIONED**

PAGE 131

Binairo

I	O	I	O	O	I	O	I	I	O	I
O	I	O	I	I	O	I	O	O	I	I
I	I	O	I	O	I	O	O	I	I	O
I	O	I	O	I	O	I	O	I	I	O
O	O	I	I	O	I	I	O	I	I	O
I	I	O	I	I	O	O	I	I	O	O
O	O	I	O	I	I	O	I	O	I	I
O	I	O	I	O	I	I	O	I	I	O
I	O	I	O	I	O	I	O	I	O	I
O	I	I	O	I	I	O	I	O	I	O
I	I	O	I	O	O	I	I	O	O	I

TRIANAGRAM • POLO/POOL

PAGE 132

Famous Hotels

H	E	L	L		P	R	I	C	E		F	L	A	M
O	N	E	A		I	N	N	E	R		L	O	M	A
M	O	N	T	E	C	A	R	L	O		O	S	A	Y
E	L	D	E	S	T		E	L	D	O	R	A	D	O
			S	T	U	D		S	E	V	E	N		
M	U	S	T	E	R	E	D		S	I	N	G	E	S
E	T	A		R	E	C	A	P		S	C	E	N	E
R	U	N	T		S	A	V	E	S		E	L	U	L
G	R	A	I	L		L	I	T	E	R		E	R	E
E	N	N	E	A	D		T	R	A	I	P	S	E	S
		T	R	I	O	S		I	N	G	A			
B	R	O	C	C	O	L	I		P	E	R	S	I	A
A	O	N	E		D	U	S	S	E	L	D	O	R	F
B	O	I	L		L	E	M	A	N		O	L	O	R
A	M	O	S		E	S	S	E	N		N	O	N	O

Answers

PAGE 133

Bargain Hunter

ST. After every vowel, there are three consecutive consonants.

DOODLE PUZZLE • HoneyComb

PAGE 134

Kakuro

3	2	9		4	5
	1	8		2	4	3
1	3	2	8		7	9
9			7	1	9
		8	1	2	
3	4	1		4	7	3
1	3			6	8

DOUBLETALK • BEACH/BEECH

PAGE 135

Two Sopranos

B	R	I	D	E		S	T	U	B		K	E	E	P
L	E	V	O	N		H	I	L	O		I	N	G	E
A	B	O	U	T		E	L	A	N		R	Y	A	N
B	A	R	B	R	A	S	T	R	E	I	S	A	N	D
			L	E	B				D	S	T			
B	E	S	E	E	C	H		A	R	T	I	S	T	S
E	G	A	D		S	A	L	T	Y		E	C	R	U
A	R	F			N	E	O				R	O	I	
T	E	E	M		I	D	O	L	S		C	U	L	T
S	T	R	E	A	M	S		L	O	V	A	B	L	E
			M	H	O			H	U	B				
J	A	M	E	S	G	A	N	D	O	L	F	I	N	I
U	P	O	N		E	S	A	U		G	A	L	E	N
N	E	A	T		N	O	N	E		A	R	Y	A	N
O	T	T	O		E	R	A	T		R	E	A	P	S

PAGE 136

Check This

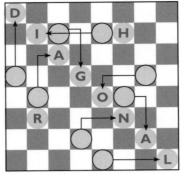

The word **DIAGONAL** can be formed. The red herrings were R and H.

PAGE 137

Horoscope

♥	$	👫	🏃	✚	♪
♪	✚	♥	$	🏃	👫
🏃	👫	✚	♪	♥	$
👫	🏃	♪	✚	$	♥
✚	♪	$	♥	👫	🏃
$	♥	🏃	👫	♪	✚

DELETE ONE • DELETE S AND FIND **CALENDAR GIRL**

FRIENDS • EACH CAN HAVE THE PREFIX BLACK- TO FORM A NEW WORD.

PAGE 138

By Leaps and Bounds

D	I	J	O	N		P	A	S	T		U	T	A	H
A	S	U	R	E		O	G	L	E		S	H	I	A
R	A	M	B	O		L	E	A	P	Y	E	A	R	S
T	O	P	I	C	A	L		V	I	O	L	I	S	T
			T	S	O	S		D	Y	E				
A	P	H	O	N	I	C		S	L	O	S	H	E	S
G	L	E	N		R	U	T	T	Y		S	I	L	L
L	A	G			P	I	E				P	G	A	
O	N	U	S		P	I	L	E	S		S	P	I	N
W	E	N	T	B	A	D		P	E	A	K	I	N	G
			E	L	Y			A	B	E	T			
S	T	U	P	O	R	S		S	U	B	T	Y	P	E
H	O	P	S	C	O	T	C	H		O	C	H	E	R
O	N	T	O		L	A	R	I		T	H	O	R	N
D	I	O	N		L	Y	O	N		T	Y	P	E	S

PAGE 139

Number Fun 2

4	x	11	–	29	+	8	=	23
x				x		+		x
10	+	2	–	8	x	5	=	20
–				x		+		
22	+	3	x	2	–	22	=	28
+		+		–		–		
8	x	5	–	53	+	40	=	27
=		=		=		=		
26		24		21		22		

DOODLE PUZZLE • BARONESS

PAGE 140

Sudoku

7	4	2	5	6	1	9	8	3
8	3	1	9	7	4	6	2	5
6	9	5	3	2	8	7	1	4
1	6	9	8	4	3	5	7	2
5	2	4	1	9	7	3	6	8
3	8	7	2	5	6	4	9	1
4	1	3	7	8	9	2	5	6
9	5	6	4	1	2	8	3	7
2	7	8	6	3	5	1	4	9

SYMBOL SUMS •
$17 - 8 \times 16 \div 2 = 72$

PAGE 141

Devilish Roles

S	E	T	S		R	A	M	B	O		E	P	I	C
A	L	O	T		E	M	E	E	R		V	E	R	A
P	E	T	E	R	F	O	N	D	A		I	T	O	N
O	N	E	R	O	U	S		S	T	U	D	E	N	T
R	A	D	I	U	S			O	M	E	R			
		L	E	A	K		P	R	A	N	C	E	R	
C	A	N	E		L	A	M	A	S		T	O	R	O
L	I	I			Z	A	G				O	T	T	
I	N	C	H		B	O	Y	E	R		I	K	E	A
O	T	H	E	L	L	O		T	E	R	N			
		O	N	E	A		C	O	F	F	I	N		
M	E	L	R	O	S	E		D	I	S	E	A	S	E
E	S	S	E		T	R	E	Y	P	A	R	K	E	R
A	M	O	I		E	S	T	E	E		N	E	R	O
T	E	N	D		D	E	E	D	S		O	R	E	L

PAGE 142

Missing Stats

Diagram 3. The orange block always moves one spot to the right and alternates between low and high.

WORD WALL •
OVERSIMPLIFICATION, ENVIRONMENTALLY, PREMEDITATED, FURNISHED, BUTTER, ASK

PAGE 143

Futoshiki

3	1	4	5	2
4	3	1	2	5
2	5 > 3	4	1
1	2	5	3	4
5 > 4 > 2 > 1	3

LETTERBLOCKS • SEVENTH/ TWELFTH

PAGE 144

Antarctica

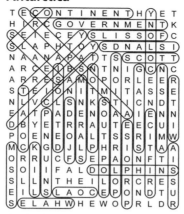

The thick ice cap on Antarctica represents 90 percent of all the ice in the world.

PAGE 145

Word Pyramid

S
(1) AS
(2) SAD
(3) AIDS
(4) IDEAS
(5) ADVISE
(6) INVADES
(7) VANISHED

PAGE 146

Fore!

PAGE 147

Artistic Roles

A	C	R	E		S	A	L	S	A		A	F	R	O
M	A	I	N		I	D	O	L	S		D	R	I	P
E	D	G	A	R	D	E	G	A	S		V	I	C	E
S	E	A	B	E	E	S		P	A	R	A	D	E	D
			L	I	S			I	O	N	A			
M	O	M	E	N	T	S		S	L	A	C	K	E	R
A	N	O		S	E	P	A	L		M	E	A	R	A
S	O	D	S		P	E	R	E	S		S	H	U	N
U	N	I	T	S		C	R	E	E	K		L	C	D
R	E	G	R	E	S	S		P	A	R	R	O	T	S
			L	E	A	P			H	O	O			
T	H	I	S	T	L	E		P	A	N	A	C	H	E
H	A	A	S		A	N	D	Y	W	A	R	H	O	L
A	N	N	E		S	T	A	L	K		E	O	N	S
R	A	I	D		H	O	M	E	S		D	U	K	E

PAGE 148

Sport Maze

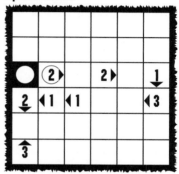

ONE LETTER LESS OR MORE • ANTITRUST

PAGE 149

Space, the Final Frontier

1. He was the first American in space
2. Space shuttle
3. Canals
4. *Saturn V*
5. The USSR launched *Sputnik* in 1957
6. The dog Laika in 1957
7. Orbit
8. She was the first woman in space
9. *Enterprise*
10. *Apollo 13*
11. *Galileo*
12. Gallifrey
13. Jupiter

Answers

Futoshiki

3	5	4	1	2
5 > 4 > 3	2 > 1
4	1 < 2	5	3
1	2	5	3	4
2 < 3	1 < 4	5

LETTERBLOCKS • FAILURE/SUCCESS

Themeless 3

A	P	E	R	S		L	A	P	D		T	H	A	T
R	O	R	E	M		A	B	R	I		A	A	R	E
B	R	I	T	I	S	H	C	O	L	U	M	B	I	A
S	E	C	U	L	A	R		D	E	T	A	I	L	S
		R	E	D			M	E	L	T				
S	C	A	N	D	A	L		I	M	P	E	A	C	H
L	A	M	S		T	U	L	S	A		S	T	O	A
O	R	B			R	I	A			I	L	L		
G	L	U	B		R	I	V	A	L		F	O	I	L
S	O	L	A	C	E	D		C	A	D	E	N	C	E
	A	S	A	S			T	W	A					
G	E	N	E	S	E	E		C	H	A	R	L	I	E
R	I	C	H	A	R	D	D	R	E	Y	F	U	S	S
O	N	E	I		V	E	R	E		N	U	B	I	A
W	E	S	T		E	R	S	E		E	L	E	N	I

Credit Rating

8. The number formed by the two first digits is always doubled. 12, 24, 48, 96, 192 on the top card and 23, 46, 92, 184, 368 on the bottom card.

BLOCK ANAGRAM • BLUE WHALE

In the Pink

O	V	E	R		S	T	A	R		A	S	C	A	P
P	O	L	A		C	O	N	E		S	C	A	L	E
E	L	E	P	H	A	N	T	S		C	H	R	I	S
R	E	C	T	O	R	Y		T	O	R	O	N	T	O
A	S	T	O	R				L	I	L	A			
		R	A	N	D		R	E	B	A	T	E	S	
A	N	C		L	A	R	G	O		E	R	I	C	H
L	E	A	H		G	E	N	U	S		S	O	H	O
M	O	D	E	M		D	U	N	E	S		N	O	W
A	N	I	S	E	E	D		D	A	H	S			
	L	I	D	O			A	C	A	S	E			
S	A	L	T	I	N	E		P	A	R	E	N	T	S
I	S	A	A	C		F	L	A	M	I	N	G	O	S
D	I	C	T	A		T	O	P	E		E	S	N	E
E	A	S	E	L		S	P	A	N		S	T	Y	X

American Graffiti

1. Ron Howard
2. Harrison Ford
3. Suzanne Somers
4. Wolfman Jack
5. Richard Dreyfuss
6. Cindy Williams
7. Mackenzie Phillips
8. Kathleen Quinlan
9. Candy Clark
10. Paul Le Mat

Spot the Differences

Slogans 1

C	E	L	S		C	A	L	E	B		E	T	C	H
A	L	E	E		L	L	A	M	A		C	H	O	U
D	O	N	T	B	E	E	V	I	L		L	I	L	T
S	I	T	T	E	R		S	T	I	P	E	N	D	S
		L	A	I	D		S	N	I	C	K			
S	C	I	E	N	C	E	S		G	E	T	S	A	T
A	L	A		S	A	R	A	H		T	I	M	E	R
L	A	M	B		L	A	T	E	R		C	A	R	E
E	R	W	I	N		T	Y	R	E	S		L	I	E
M	A	H	L	E	R		R	E	C	A	L	L	E	D
	A	L	L	E	Y		S	E	L	A				
A	N	T	I	L	L	E	S		I	M	P	A	L	A
B	A	I	O		I	N	N	O	V	A	T	I	O	N
C	L	A	N		S	T	A	L	E		O	D	I	N
D	A	M	S		H	A	G	A	R		P	A	N	E

Concentration—To a T

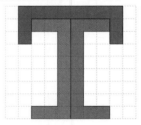

WORD WALL • OVERSIMPLIFICATION, RESOURCEFULNESS, MERETRICIOUS, CENTRALLY, THRUMS, ANY

PAGE 158

Sudoku Twin

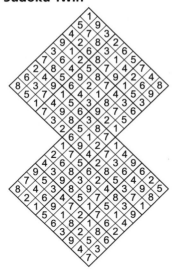

DELETE ONE • DELETE T AND ENJOY **SAINT PATRICK'S DAY**

PAGE 159

Big Bands

PAGE 160

Smacker

Lips 4 and 7.

LETTERBLOCKS • DIGITAL/ NETWORK

PAGE 161

Anagram Mountain

Level 1
Vat
Next
Party
Exodus

Level 2
Oblique
Heraldic
Costumer
Beefsteak

Level 3
Voyeuristic
Rhododendron
Brainstorming
Autobiographic

PAGE 162

Slogans 2

PAGE 163

Stop-and-Go Anagrams

LEVEL 1
Porthole
Glossary
Computer

LEVEL 2
Creative, reactive
Unloaded, duodenal
Latitude, altitude

LEVEL 3
Recounts, construe, counters, trounces
Staplers, plasters, psalters
Triangle, altering, alerting, integral, relating

PAGE 164

The Well-Read Reader

1. **c.** J. K. Rowling
2. **c.** Charles V
3. **b.** China
4. **a.** *Better Homes and Garden Cook Book*
5. **b.** Carrie
6. **c.** Salman Rushdie
7. **b.** They've all been used to challenge the First Amendment
8. **a.** Barbara Ehrenreich
9. **c.** Madonna
10. **a.** Meatpacking

PAGE 165

Flag It Up

ZFG. Starting with Q, each subsequent flag is divided into one more color pattern area.

DOUBLETALK • FINISH/FINNISH

PAGE 166

M*A*S*H

Answers

PAGE 167

Sudoku X

7	5	3	8	2	6	1	9	4
4	1	8	5	7	9	6	3	2
6	2	9	4	3	1	5	7	8
1	8	5	3	4	7	2	6	9
9	4	2	6	8	5	3	1	7
3	7	6	9	1	2	8	4	5
5	9	1	7	6	8	4	2	3
8	6	4	2	9	3	7	5	1
2	3	7	1	5	4	9	8	6

BLOCK ANAGRAM • CLARESSA SHIELDS

PAGE 168

Binairo

I	I	0	0	I	I	0	I	0	0	I	0
0	I	I	0	I	I	0	I	0	I	0	0
I	0	0	I	0	0	I	0	I	I	0	I
I	0	I	I	0	I	0	I	0	0	I	0
0	I	0	0	I	I	0	I	I	0	I	0
I	I	0	I	0	0	I	0	0	I	0	I
0	0	I	0	I	I	0	I	0	I	0	I
I	I	0	0	I	0	0	I	0	I	0	I
0	0	I	I	0	0	I	0	I	0	I	I
0	0	I	I	0	I	I	0	I	I	0	0
I	I	0	0	I	0	0	I	0	0	I	I
0	0	I	0	I	0	I	0	I	I	0	I

TRIANAGRAM • ALERT/LATER

PAGE 169

Blooms

Flower branch 2. The top flower of all the other branches has just as many petals as flowers on the branch.

QUICK CROSSWORD •

PAGE 170

Hairstyles

PAGE 171

Cocktails

Burning cocktails contain a small quantity of high-percentage alcohol that is lit before being served.

PAGE 172

Movie Drunks

PAGE 173

Greener Grass

Zone 6. All zones with four intersections are colored in.

QUICK WORD SEARCH •

PAGE 174

Sudoku

1	2	7	3	4	5	8	6	9
9	3	6	8	1	2	7	4	5
4	8	5	7	9	6	1	3	2
5	1	9	2	8	3	6	7	4
2	7	4	1	6	9	3	5	8
3	6	8	5	7	4	9	2	1
8	4	1	6	5	7	2	9	3
6	9	3	4	2	8	5	1	7
7	5	2	9	3	1	4	8	6

SYMBOL SUMS •
24 + 4 X 6 ÷ 4 = 42

PAGE 175
Sport Maze

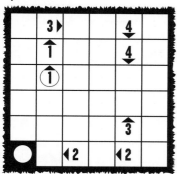

ONE LETTER LESS OR MORE • STRIKEOUT

PAGE 176
Word Sudoku

W	I	N	E	R	O	V	K	L
R	O	K	I	V	L	W	E	N
V	E	L	N	K	W	R	I	O
K	W	I	V	L	N	E	O	R
L	V	R	O	E	I	N	W	K
E	N	O	K	W	R	L	V	I
N	K	E	R	O	V	I	L	W
O	R	W	L	I	E	K	N	V
I	L	V	W	N	K	O	R	E

UNCANNY TURN • ENRAGED

PAGE 177
Song Tributes

O	L	L	A		H	I	N	D	U		S	T	E	P
S	E	A	M		A	D	O	R	N		T	I	R	E
C	A	S	E	Y	J	O	N	E	S		A	M	I	E
A	S	T	R	O				S	T	A	M	M	E	R
R	E	S	I	G	N	S		S	O	N	I	C		
			C	A	P	P			P	I	N	G	E	D
N	A	J	A		R	A	F	T	S		A	R	I	A
A	G	A			W	B	A				A	R	M	
N	O	M	E		S	N	I	P	E		A	W	E	E
A	G	E	N	D	A		E	V	E	N				
	S	T	U	N	S		R	E	A	D	M	I	T	
A	D	D	E	N	D	A			C	R	A	S	H	
B	E	E	R		B	U	D	D	Y	H	O	L	L	Y
A	L	A	E		A	N	D	R	E		I	T	E	M
T	E	N	D		G	A	T	E	S		D	A	T	E

PAGE 178
Themeless 4

P	O	E	M	S		C	N	B	C		C	E	L	T
E	L	S	I	E		L	A	L	A		O	P	A	H
C	O	A	S	T		A	H	A	B		L	I	S	A
K	R	I	S	T	I	Y	A	M	A	G	U	C	H	I
			I	L	A			R	E	M				
S	T	E	V	E	N	S	P	I	E	L	B	E	R	G
O	R	L	E		S	C	A	N	T		O	N	E	R
N	A	E			E	D	T			A	B	O	
I	S	N	T		I	N	R	E	D		A	M	E	S
C	H	A	R	A	C	T	E	R	I	S	T	I	C	S
		O	W	E			S	A	T					
D	A	N	I	E	L	R	A	D	C	L	I	F	F	E
E	R	I	K		A	O	N	E		U	R	I	A	L
E	T	N	A		N	A	N	A		T	E	T	R	A
D	Y	E	S		D	R	E	D		E	D	S	E	L

PAGE 179
Keep Going

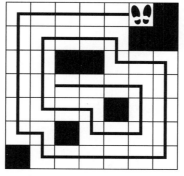

PAGE 180
Number Crunch

9	1	7	3	5	2	8		9	2	6	9	5	8	2
2	3	4	6	4	5	3		5	4	3	1	7	4	7
6	8	1	5	8	2	8		6	7	3	9	3	6	8
9	8	7	9		9	2	1	6		9	5	2	9	
2	3	6		5	4	7	0	3	1	1	0	7	8	6
8	1	9	9	7		2	3	9	3	0	7			
4	5	1	0	2	8	4	6		5	2	6	9	8	5
6	2	7	1	4	8	8		8	4	7	4	3	1	6
9	3	9	9	6	2		7	5	0	1	6	0	1	4
			1	2	3	8	3	0		7	0	2	5	3
7	4	9	6	5	7	1	2	0	5	0		6	0	1
2	8	1	0		4	4	7	5		9	4	0	4	
6	2	5	5	1	4	0		8	0	1	7	3	4	8
9	6	1	7	0	0	6		2	0	6	8	1	5	7
4	0	0	3	7	6	5		5	4	3	8	3	0	2

PAGE 181
Bach to the Classics

1. **b.** "Sabre Dance"
2. **a.** Johann Strauss
3. **b.** 1812
4. **a.** Loud
5. **c.** Symphony No. 5
6. **b.** Salzburg
7. **b.** Clarinet
8. **a.** Soprano
9. **b.** New York Philharmonic Orchestra
10. **c.** Prima donna

PAGE 182
Hidden Theme

S	E	L	E	S		M	O	O	G		A	B	E	L
U	L	E	N	T		E	U	R	O		N	O	T	A
M	O	N	T	E	C	A	R	L	O		I	N	R	I
S	N	A	R	L	E	D		E	D	A	S	N	E	R
			E	L	L			N	O	T	E			
A	P	P	E	A	L	S		B	E	L	O	V	E	D
G	R	A	S			C	A	R	S		N	I	L	E
N	O	R			C	A	P	O	S			L	I	N
E	L	K	S		O	R	E	O			A	L	O	T
W	E	A	P	O	N	S		M	U	P	P	E	T	S
			V	E	R	N			S	I	P			
E	R	E	C	T	E	D		M	A	L	A	I	S	E
R	E	N	I		C	A	L	I	F	O	R	N	I	A
B	L	U	E		T	S	A	R		T	E	L	L	S
E	Y	E	S		S	H	O	E		S	L	A	K	E

PAGE 183

Sudoku Twin

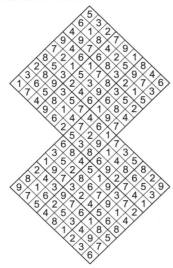

DELETE ONE • DELETE S AND FIND **ACADEMY AWARDS**

PAGE 184

Sunny

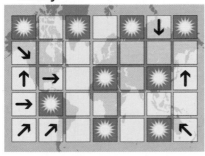

TRIANAGRAM • HEALS/HALES

PAGE 185

Holiday Carols

PAGE 186

Rack 'Em

02	03	25	19
08	31	06	04
16	01	11	21
23	14	07	05

DOUBLETALK • **SOME/SUM**

PAGE 187

Binairo

0	0	1	0	1	1	0	1	0	1	1
0	1	0	1	1	0	1	0	1	0	1
1	0	1	1	0	1	0	0	1	1	0
1	1	0	0	1	0	1	1	0	0	1
0	0	1	1	0	1	0	1	1	0	1
0	1	1	0	1	0	1	0	1	1	0
1	1	0	1	0	1	0	1	0	0	1
1	0	1	0	0	1	1	0	1	1	0
0	1	0	0	1	0	1	1	0	1	1
1	0	1	1	0	1	0	1	1	0	0
1	1	0	1	1	0	1	0	0	1	0

TRIANAGRAM •
SALESMEN/NAMELESS

PAGE 188

Namesakes 1

PAGE 189

Flying High

1. Charles Lindbergh
2. The Hudson River
3. The first black female pilot in the United States. She trained in Paris and received her license in 1921.
4. No liquids or gels would be permitted
5. Amelia Earhart
6. The British and French
7. Mumbai
8. Five
9. Canard
10. Concordski
11. The Comet
12. It was the first aircraft ever to fly into space, in 1967.
13. The SR-71 Blackbird spy plane
14. By escaping from an airplane by parachute. The club was named after the silkworm (caterpillar) that provided the parachute silk.

PAGE 190
Word Sudoku

H	V	S	N	T	A	D	E	I
T	E	D	V	H	I	S	A	N
I	N	A	E	D	S	T	V	H
S	A	V	D	E	N	H	I	T
E	I	T	H	S	V	N	D	A
D	H	N	I	A	T	E	S	V
V	D	I	T	N	E	A	H	S
A	T	H	S	V	D	I	N	E
N	S	E	A	I	H	V	T	D

UNCANNY TURN • DONE

PAGE 191
Namesakes 2

C	H	A	N		P	E	D	A	L		S	H	A	W
A	O	N	E		R	O	U	G	E		H	E	R	O
L	U	K	E	D	O	N	A	L	D		E	N	Y	O
E	R	A	S	E	D		D	O	G	G	E	R	E	L
		O	N	U	S		W	E	E	P	Y			
C	O	N	N	E	C	T	S		R	E	D	A	C	T
A	L	I		B	E	A	T	S		K	O	A	L	A
R	I	G	A		S	T	R	I	P		G	R	I	P
O	V	E	R	T		E	E	R	I	E		O	N	A
M	E	L	T	E	D		P	E	N	N	A	N	T	S
	B	I	T	E	S		D	O	O	R				
M	E	R	C	H	A	N	T		C	L	A	I	R	E
E	L	U	L		R	A	Y	C	H	A	R	L	E	S
R	I	C	E		E	R	R	O	L		A	I	N	T
V	E	E	S		R	E	E	S	E		T	A	T	E

PAGE 192-193
Healthy Appetites

A. Brian Willard – pineapple first, blueberry second

B. Ewan Potter – blackcurrant first, syrup second

C. David Symes – syrup first, pineapple second

D. Adam Lowe – strawberry first, banana second

E. Fred Robertson – banana first, lemon second

F. Graham Veness – blueberry first, strawberry second

PAGE 194
Missing Script

6. Read from left to right alternating two digits from the upper and lower rows as a series of numbers that are always divided by two. 96 ÷ 2 = 48 ÷ 2 = 24 ÷ 2 = 12 ÷ 2 = 06.

BLOCK ANAGRAM• LAKE STURGEON

PAGE 195
Sandwich Shop

A	S	C	A	P		B	A	R	D		A	C	T	S
B	L	A	M	E		A	B	E	E		S	H	O	E
C	O	R	N	E	D	B	E	E	F		T	E	L	L
		E	P	E	E		F	E	R	R	E	L	L	
D	A	M	S	E	L		N	O	I	S	E	S		
A	V	O	I	D	E	D		A	S	I	D	E		
N	A	N	A		S	E	I	N	E		E	S	S	E
N	I	T			B	L	T			T	I	A		
O	L	E	G		G	R	E	E	N		P	E	E	R
	C	L	A	R	A		D	E	F	I	A	N	T	
M	A	R	I	N	O		H	O	O	K	A	H		
A	N	I	S	T	O	N		A	R	O	N			
H	O	S	T		M	U	F	F	U	L	E	T	T	A
A	L	T	E		E	D	D	A		E	E	R	I	E
N	E	O	N		D	E	A	R		D	R	Y	E	R

PAGE 196
Beatlemania

M	A	M	A		A	D	A	M		D	E	S	E	X
A	D	I	T		R	O	N	A		O	C	H	R	E
Y	E	S	T	E	R	D	A	Y		C	H	E	S	S
O	N	T	A	R	I	O		A	T	T	E	S	T	
			C	I	V			I	O	L	A			
T	O	W	H	E	A	D		A	R	R	O	W	S	
A	C	H	E		L	O	R	R	E		N	O	N	O
T	A	A			O	U	I			M	A	P		
A	L	T	O		C	R	E	E	P		P	A	R	E
	A	G	R	E	E	S		L	E	A	R	N	E	D
	O	L	A	N			D	R	E					
B	E	A	S	T	S		E	D	U	C	A	T	E	
H	A	S	N	T		T	E	L	L	M	E	W	H	Y
A	N	O	D	E		L	O	S	E		D	O	E	R
T	E	N	O	R		O	N	E	R		E	L	E	E

PAGE 197
Reel Them In!

1. True
2. False
3. True
4. False
5. False
6. True
7. False
8. True
9. True
10 False

PAGE 198
Mixed Drinks

B	A	R	A		A	K	I	T	A		S	P	O	T
E	L	I	S		T	I	D	E	S		K	I	T	E
T	O	M	C	O	L	L	I	N	S		E	N	O	S
S	T	A	R	M	A	N		S	U	R	P	A	S	S
			I	N	N			R	O	T	C			
R	A	B	B	I	T	S		S	E	N	I	O	R	S
I	D	L	E		A	C	R	I	D		C	L	A	W
C	O	O			A	A	R			A	V	A		
C	R	O	C		G	R	E	E	D		A	D	E	N
I	N	D	O	O	R	S		S	I	G	N	A	L	S
	Y	U	M	A			S	E	I					
B	U	M	P	I	N	G		E	D	A	S	N	E	R
O	R	A	L		D	R	Y	M	A	R	T	I	N	I
O	G	R	E		M	I	A	M	I		O	N	I	T
K	E	Y	S		A	M	M	A	N		N	O	D	E

PAGE 199
Sudoku

9	2	4	3	7	5	1	8	6
6	1	8	4	9	2	3	5	7
5	7	3	6	8	1	4	2	9
7	3	2	5	4	6	9	1	8
8	6	1	7	3	9	2	4	5
4	5	9	2	1	8	6	7	3
1	4	6	9	5	7	8	3	2
2	8	5	1	6	3	7	9	4
3	9	7	8	2	4	5	6	1

SYMBOL SUMS •
4 ÷ 2 X 14 − 7 = 21

ANSWERS TO DO YOU KNOW?

p. 10:	Bob Dylan
p. 18:	Madagascar
p. 20:	Evonne Goolagong
p. 26:	Gustav Klimt
p. 38:	Giacomo Puccini
p. 43:	Albertville, France
p. 54:	Neoclassical
p. 62:	The island of Mauritius (east of Madagascar in the Indian Ocean)
p. 68:	Basketball
p. 71:	*Villette* by Charlotte Brontë
p. 77:	Denmark
p. 82:	Sir Ludwig Guttmann
p. 88:	Atticus Finch
p. 100:	Scotland
p. 102:	Nitrogen
p. 108:	Queen Scheherazade (she tells the stories to stave off her execution by the King)
p. 110:	Mexico
p. 112:	Pacific and Atlantic
p. 116:	Auguste Rodin
p. 125:	The Alps
p. 131:	Smallpox vaccine
p. 136:	Benny, Björn, Agnetha and Anni-Frid
p. 140:	Bluetooth technology
p. 145:	Platypus
p. 148:	Uruguay
p. 150:	Veins
p. 155:	Florence, Italy
p. 157:	Pacific
p. 167:	Ferns
p. 168:	Tutankhamun's tomb
p. 175:	Frisbee
p. 179:	Coca-Cola
p. 187:	Minotaur
p. 190:	Joan Fontaine
p. 199:	Wisconsin

ANSWERS TO TRIVIA

p. 18:	Rainier III, Prince of Monaco
p. 21:	Maksymilian Faktorowicz
p. 27:	Tatum O'Neal
p. 35:	Professor James Moriarty
p. 49:	Matt Groenig
p. 59:	Whitney Houston
p. 62:	Liza Minnelli
p. 78:	Veronica Lake
p. 101:	Henry Mancini
p. 110:	Bobsledding
p. 118:	Coco Chanel
p. 122:	Dr. Seuss
p. 128:	Eldrick Tont Woods
p. 134:	Pete Best
p. 139:	1994
p. 143:	Anthony Perkins
p. 155:	Stevie Wonder
p. 163:	Goneril, Regan and Cordelia
p. 174:	Charlie Chaplin
p. 176:	Stephen King
p. 180:	Ben Kingsley
p. 181:	Benjamin Britten
p. 197:	A Walking Fish (Ambulatory Fish)

CREDITS

Cover photo credit:
The Noun Project

Credits:

Illustrations unless noted below: BrainSnack®

David Bodycombe: 136, 161, 163, 180

Emily Cox & Henry Rathvon: 12, 41, 65, 91, 113

Maggie Ellis: 66, 69, 109, 138

Peter Frank: Binairo, Kakuro, Number Cluster, Sudoku, Word Searches, Word Sudoku

Jean Griffing: 14, 42, 135, 188, 191

Cindy Lather: 153

Linda Lather: 89, 92, 95

Don Law: 39

Mary Leonard: 86, 123, 132

Myles Mellor: 159, 166, 185

Brian O'Shea: 195

Peggy O'Shea: 25, 36

Karen Peterson: 55, 80

Puzzlemakers: 119, 192-193

John M. Samson: 8, 47, 103, 106, 117, 141, 147, 177, 182, 196

Michele Sayer: 11, 19, 75, 156, 162

Justin Scroggie: 26, 139

Jim Sears: 120, 126, 151, 178

Debra Steilen: 60, 105, 154

Tim Wagner: 28, 31, 50, 172, 198

Darren Walsh: 59

Cindy Wheeler: 58, 63

Kelly Whitt: 72, 83, 98, 114, 170